INVARIANT THEORY

MATHEMATICS LECTURE NOTE SERIES

E. Artin and J. Tate	CLASS FIELD THEORY
Michael Atiyah	K-THEORY
Hyman Bass	ALGEBRAIC K-THEORY
Melvyn S. Berger Marion S. Berger	PERSPECTIVES IN NONLINEARITY
Armand Borel	LINEAR ALGEBRA GROUPS
Andrew Browder	INTRODUCTION TO FUNCTION ALGEBRAS
Paul J. Cohen	SET THEORY AND THE CONTINUUM HYPOTHESIS
Eldon Dyer	COHOMOLOGY THEORIES
Walter Feit	CHARACTERS OF FINITE GROUPS
John Fogarty	INVARIANT THEORY
William Fulton	ALGEBRAIC CURVES
Marvin J. Greenberg	LECTURES ON ALGEBRAIC TOPOLOGY
Marvin J. Greenberg	LECTURES ON FORMS IN MANY VARIABLES
Robin Hartshorne	FOUNDATIONS OF PROJECTIVE GEOMETRY
J. F. P. Hudson	PIECEWISE LINEAR TOPOLOGY
Irving Kaplansky	RINGS OF OPERATORS
K. Kapp and H. Schneider	COMPLETELY O-SIMPLE SEMIGROUPS
Joseph B. Keller Stuart Antman	BIFURCATION THEORY AND NONLINEAR EIGENVALUE PROBLEMS
Serge Lang	ALGEBRAIC FUNCTIONS
Serge Lang	RAPPORT SUR LA COHOMOLOGIE DES GROUPES
Ottmar Loos	SYMMETRIC SPACES I: GENERAL THEORY II: COMPACT SPACES AND CLASSIFICATION

A Note from the Publisher

This volume was printed directly from a typescript prepared by the author, who takes full responsibility for its content and appearance. The Publisher has not performed his usual functions of reviewing, editing, typesetting, and proofreading the material prior to publication.

The Publisher fully endorses this informal and quick method of publishing lecture notes at a moderate price, and he wishes to thank the author for preparing the material for publication.

INVARIANT THEORY

JOHN FOGARTY

University of Pennsylvania

W. A. BENJAMIN, INC.

New York Amsterdam

1969

INVARIANT THEORY

Library of Congress Catalog Card Number 79-81997
Manufactured in the United States of America
12345M32109

*The manuscript was put into production on March 1, 1969;
this volume was published on May 1, 1969*

W. A. BENJAMIN, INC.
New York, New York 10016

To

Oscar Zariski

on the occasion of his

seventieth birthday

PREFACE

The present notes are devoted to a reasonably exhaustive discussion of the basic qualitative problem of algebraic invariant theory, viz., given a ring R and a group G of automorphisms of R, to describe the ring of G-invariant elements of R. In particular, if R is a finitely generated commutative algebra over the field k and each element of G leaves the elements of k fixed, then is the ring of invariants also a finitely generated algebra over k? This is essentially the famous fourteenth problem of Hilbert. We shall not concern ourselves with the quantitative aspects of the problem, e.g., given generators and relations for R, to obtain the same for the ring of invariants.

Why should one be interested in such a problem, aside from its intrinsic simplicity and natural appeal? One reason is that it is closely related to what might be called the classification problem. This can be stated in very general terms as follows. Given a collection of mathematical objects of a certain type, and a well defined notion of 'equivalence' or 'isomorphism' between these objects, can one find a natural mathematical structure for the set of isomorphism classes of objects of the given type?

Let us look quickly at one example. By an algebra over the field k we mean a vector space A over k, plus a bilinear mapping $M : A \times A \rightarrow A$. Suppose we seek to classify all algebras of dimension d over k, up to isomorphism. Clearly we may fix the underlying vector space A. Then the set of all algebra structures on A is simply the vector space of all k-bilinear maps from $A \times A$ to A. Two such structures M' and M'' are isomorphic if and only if there is a k-linear isomorphism $T : A \rightarrow A$ such that $M'(Tx,Ty) = T(M''(x,y))$, for all $x,y \in A$.

If B denotes the space of bilinear maps from $A \times A$ to A and $GL(A)$ the group of k-linear automorphisms of A, then $GL(A)$ acts by linear transformations on B via: $M^T(x,y) = M(Tx,Ty)$, $T \in GL(A)$, $M \in B$. The isomorphism classes of such structures are then in bijective correspondence with the orbits of this action of $GL(A)$ on B. The problem now becomes one of finding a 'reasonable' structure for the set of orbits.

If R is the ring of polynomial functions on B - the symmetric algebra of B^* - then the elements of R invariant under the induced action of $GL(A)$ on R can be regarded as functions on the set of orbits. The problem of invariants and the orbit space problem are thus intimately related.

The first chapter is a utilitarian introduction to affine algebraic geometry over an algebraically closed field. Because we confine ourselves to affine geometry, we must leave aside the relation of invariant theory to projective geometry. In any case, the latter theory deserves a volume to itself.

The second chapter is more detailed, vis-a-vis its subject matter - affine algebraic groups - than the first. We obtain some fairly deep general results on these groups, e.g., we construct the quotient of an affine group by a closed normal subgroup. This quotient turns out to be itself an affine group - a highly non-trivial result requiring invariantive methods for its proof.

In the foregoing chapters our methods are strictly 'global', i.e., we deal with whole 'varieties' at a time. However, 'infinitesimal' methods are often more powerful than global ones, and it is in the third chapter that we introduce them. The idea behind these methods is very simple, and comes down in our case to this. Suppose that the base field is the complex numbers and that a 'continuous' group G operates on a vector space by linear transformations. If a vector $v \in V$ is invariant under this action, then the assertion

$$\frac{\partial}{\partial g}(gv) = 0, \qquad g \in G,$$

is extraordinarily suggestive. The problem is to make it precise. Making use of the algebraic version of derivatives, we show that there is a natural way to attach to each affine group a finite dimensional algebra - called the Lie algebra of the group - which in the arcane language of the nineteenth century is very aptly described as the group of 'infinitesimal transformations' of the given group. Whenever the group acts on a vector space by linear transformations, so does its Lie algebra. Since the Lie algebra is a 'linear' object, whereas the group itself almost always is not, the use of the Lie algebra to analyze the given action eases the task immeasurably. There is, however, one flaw in this seemingly ideal situation. It goes completely awry in positive characteristics. This is perhaps the major reason why invariant theory over modular fields is almost completely uncharted territory.

The fourth chapter digresses to develop the Cartan-Weyl representation theory of Lie algebras in characteristic zero. This is the technical groundwork upon which the invariant theory in characteristic zero is laid. We include a conclusive set of counterexamples to the Cartan-Weyl theory in characteristic p.

In the final chapter, we reap the fruits of our efforts. We give a complete solution of the Hilbert fourteenth problem for semisimple groups in characteristic zero - due to Weyl - and a complete solution of the orbit space problem for such groups - due to Mumford.

After this, we turn to a more detailed study of the structure of affine groups, enabling us to put our invariantive results in more definitive form. Next we prove some recent results of Nagata and Seshadri on so-called 'semi-reductive' groups - a concept which affords the only general method now available for invariant theory in positive characteristics. We conclude with some results of Weitzenbock and Fischer which, from the viewpoint of the theory as developed today, appear rather isolated, but which may conceal general techniques.

A number of exercises are scattered throughout the text and some supplementary ones are given at the end of the book, but I have made no effort to give full coverage in this respect. Since no familiarity with algebraic geometry is assumed, I have included proofs of all the technical algebraic results needed in the course of the development.

I have, of course, borrowed heavily from many writers in preparing this material. In particular, I have relied upon Serre's "Lie Algebras and Lie Groups" (Benjamin 1965), Nagata's "Lectures on the Fourteenth Problem of Hilbert" (Tata Institute, 1965) and Mumford's "Geometric Invariant Theory" (Springer, 1965)

D. S. Rim has kindly made available to me his unpublished lecture notes on Lie algebras and I am indebted to him for many of the examples that appear here. I should also acknowledge what I have been taught by S.Sternberg, and, above all, by O. Zariski.

The text itself is an elaboration on lecture notes that were prepared for a course in modern invariant theory at the University of Pennsylvania in the spring of 1968. I owe much to the patient criticism of the students who attended those lectures.

JOHN FOGARTY

Philadelphia
February 1969

CONTENTS

PREFACE ix

CHAPTER I AFFINE ALGEBRAIC SETS

1. Algebraic sets in affine space 1
2. Affine algebraic sets in abstracto 7
3. Noetherian rings 14
4. Decomposition of affine algebraic sets 20
5. Products of affine algebraic sets 22
6. Examples of affine algebraic sets 31
7. The function field of an affine variety 38

CHAPTER II AFFINE ALGEBRAIC GROUPS

1. Affine groups 41
2. Examples of affine groups 46
3. Actions 50
4. Quotients 55
5. Representations of affine groups 58
6. Quotients of affine groups by closed normal subgroups 66

CHAPTER III AFFINE GROUPS AND LIE ALGEBRAS

1. Some local algebra 79
2. Derivations and Lie algebras 85
3. The Lie algebra of an affine group 90
4. Dimension theory 95
5. Functorial properties of the Lie algebra 103

CHAPTER IV REPRESENTATIONS OF LIE ALGEBRAS

1. Complete reducibility 113
2. The theorems of Engel and Lie 116
3. Cartan's criterion 123
4. Semisimple Lie algebras 128
5. Weyl's theorem 135
6. Reductive Lie algebras 143
7. Counterexamples in characteristic p 147

CHAPTER V INVARIANTS OF AFFINE GROUPS

1. Hilbert's fourteenth problem 151
2. The Reynolds operator 154
3. Mumford's theorem 159
4. Semisimple groups revisited 162
5. Solvable groups 171
6. Integral dependence and finiteness 180
7. Finite groups 186
8. Semi-reductive groups 188
9. The normalization of an affine variety 196
10. Weitzenbock's theorem 201
11. Fischer's theorem 205

Miscellaneous exercises 206

CHAPTER I

AFFINE ALGEBRAIC SETS

I-1 ALGEBRAIC SETS IN AFFINE SPACE

We fix, once and for all, an algebraically closed field k, making no assumption about the characteristic of k. Let $\underline{A}^n$ denote the affine space $k^n = k \times \cdots \times k$ (n factors). $\underline{A}^n$ is a vector space over k, but for the moment, this fact will play a subordinate role.

If $F = F(X_1,\ldots,X_n)$ is a polynomial in the n variables $X_1,\ldots,X_n$ with coefficients in k, we say that the point $x = (x_1,\ldots,x_n)$ in $\underline{A}^n$ is a zero of F if $F(x_1,\ldots,x_n) = 0$. The set of zeroes of F is called the locus of F, and is denoted by $\underline{V}(F)$. A subset V of $\underline{A}^n$ is called a hypersurface in $\underline{A}^n$ if it is the locus of a non-constant polynomial.

Let $k[\underline{A}^n]$ denote the ring $k[X_1,\ldots,X_n]$ of polynomials in $X_1,\ldots,X_n$ with coefficients in k. If B is a subset of $\underline{A}^n$, the set of $F \in k[\underline{A}^n]$

such that $F(x) = 0$ for all $x \in B$ is an ideal in $k[\underline{A}^n]$ which we denote by $\underline{I}_{\underline{A}^n}(B)$, or simply by $\underline{I}(B)$. Conversely, if I is an ideal in $k[\underline{A}^n]$, the set of $x \in \underline{A}^n$ such that $F(x) = 0$ for all $F \in I$ is called the <u>locus of</u> I in $\underline{A}^n$, and denoted by $\underline{V}_{\underline{A}^n}(I)$, or simply by $\underline{V}(I)$. If S is any subset of $k[\underline{A}^n]$ then the set of all $x \in \underline{A}^n$ such that $F(x) = 0$ for all $F \in S$ is the locus of an ideal in $k[\underline{A}^n]$, viz., the ideal generated by S. In other words, $\bigcap_{F \in S} \underline{V}(F) = \underline{V}(I)$, where I is the ideal generated by S.

EXERCISE. Verify the following assertions. Here, I and J denote ideals in $k[\underline{A}^n]$ and B and C denote subsets of $\underline{A}^n$.

i) $I \subset J$ implies $\underline{V}(J) \subset \underline{V}(I)$.

ii) $B \subset C$ implies $\underline{I}(C) \subset \underline{I}(B)$.

iii) $\underline{I}(B \cup C) = \underline{I}(B) \cap \underline{I}(C)$.

iv) If $I + J = \{F + G : F \in I,\ G \in J\}$, then $I + J$ is an ideal in $k[\underline{A}^n]$ and $\underline{V}(I + J) = \underline{V}(I) \cap \underline{V}(J)$.

v) If $IJ = \{\sum F_i G_i : F_i \in I, G_i \in J\}$, then IJ is an ideal in $k[\underline{A}^n]$ and $\underline{V}(IJ) = \underline{V}(I \cap J) = \underline{V}(I) \cup \underline{V}(J)$.

vi) $V((0)) = \underline{A}^n$, and $V((1)) = \emptyset$.

Also $\underline{I}(\underline{A}^n) = (0)$, and $\underline{I}(\emptyset) = (1)$.

vii) $\underline{V}(\underline{I}(B)) \supset B$, and $\underline{I}(\underline{V}(I)) \supset I$.

viii) $\underline{I}(\underline{V}(I)) = I$ if and only if $F^n \in I$ implies $F \in I$ for all $n > 0$, and all $F \in k[\underline{A}^n]$.

DEFINITION 1.1. A subset V of $\underline{A}^n$ is called an <u>algebraic</u> <u>set</u> <u>in</u> $\underline{A}^n$ if and only if $V = \underline{V}(I(V))$.

This means that V is an algebraic set in $\underline{A}^n$ if and only if V is the locus of some ideal in $k[\underline{A}^n]$. We note that two ideals in $k[\underline{A}^n]$ may very well have the same locus in $\underline{A}^n$ without being the same. Conversely, if B and C are subsets of $\underline{A}^n$, $\underline{I}(B) = \underline{I}(C)$ does <u>not</u> imply that $B = C$. However if B and C are algebraic sets then this cannot happen, i.e., $\underline{I}(B) = \underline{I}(C)$ implies $B = C$. According to what we have said above, every algebraic set in $\underline{A}^n$ is an intersection of hypersurfaces, viz., if V is an algebraic set, then

$$V = \bigcap_{F \in \underline{I}(V)} \underline{V}(F).$$

We now topologize A^1 by taking as closed sets the finite sets together with $\underline{A}^1$ and the empty set. Note that this topology is very coarse, i.e., there are comparatively few closed sets. Now we can regard each $F \in k[\underline{A}^n]$ as a mapping of $\underline{A}^n$ into $\underline{A}^1$. On $\underline{A}^n$, the coarsest topology such that all these mappings are continuous is called the Zariski topology. This means that the Zariski topology is completely determined by the ring $k[\underline{A}^n]$ of k-valued functions on $\underline{A}^n$.

PROPOSITION 1.2. A subset B of $\underline{A}^n$ is closed in the Zariski topology if and only if B is an algebraic set. In fact, the complements of hypersurfaces form a basis for the open sets in the Zariski topology on $\underline{A}^n$.

Proof: Since every proper algebraic set in $\underline{A}^n$ is an intersection of hypersurfaces, and conversely, it suffices to prove the second assertion. However it is clear that $\underline{V}(FG) = \underline{V}(F) \cup \underline{V}(G)$ for all $F, G \in k[\underline{A}^n]$. This means that the hypersurfaces are closed under finite unions. Therefore the weakest topology on $\underline{A}^n$ such that all $F \in k[\underline{A}^n]$ determine continuous mappings is just the one whose closed sets are arbitrary intersections of hypersurfaces.

Henceforth, the terms "closed" and "open"

will refer exclusively to the Zariski topology. If V is a closed subset of $\underline{A}^n$, i.e., an algebraic set in $\underline{A}^n$, then V inherits a topology from $\underline{A}^n$, viz., $Z \subset V$ is closed if and only if there exists a closed subset W of $\underline{A}^n$ such that $Z = V \cap W$. This topology on V will also be called the Zariski topology.

If V is a closed subset of $\underline{A}^n$ let $I = \underline{I}(V)$. Then for any $F, G \in k[\underline{A}^n]$, $F|V = G|V$ if and only if $F - G \in I$. Thus $k[\underline{A}^n]/I$ may be regarded as a ring of k-valued function on V. We denote this ring by $k[V]$ and call it the <u>coordinate</u> <u>ring</u> of V.

The following theorem - known as Hilbert's nullstellensatz - is the cornerstone for our entire development. Since the proof which we give uses ideas that are only introduced in chapter V, the reader may omit the proof on a first reading without prejudicing his comprehension of what follows.

THEOREM A. If I is an ideal in $k[\underline{A}^n]$, then $\underline{V}(I) = \emptyset$ if and only if $I = (1)$.

<u>Proof</u>: If $I = (1)$ then $\underline{V}(1) = \emptyset$, as we have already noted. The converse statement is the hard part. We must prove that if I is a proper ideal in $k[\underline{A}^n]$, then there is at least one point $x \in \underline{A}^n$

such that $F(x) = 0$ for all $F \in I$. Clearly, if we can prove this when I is maximal, then we are finished.

Now let I be a maximal ideal in $k[\underline{A}^n] = k[X_1,\ldots,X_n]$. Let x_i denote the residue of X_i modulo I. Now if $F \in I$, then certainly $F(x_1,\ldots,x_n) = 0$. (This is a trivial formality). On the other hand, since I is maximal, the ring $k[\underline{A}^n]/I$ is a field - containing k. If we can show that this field is k itself, then it will follow that the n-tuple $(x_1,\ldots,x_n)$ is a point of $\underline{A}^n$, and we are done! Thus the theorem boils down to the following lemma of Zariski:

LEMMA: If K is a field (not necessarily algebraically closed) and if the ring $K[x_1,\ldots,x_n]$ is a field, then the x_i are algebraic over K.

Proof: We use induction on n. If $n = 1$, then x_1 cannot be transcendental over K since in that case, $K[x_1]$ is isomorphic to the ring of polynomials in one variable, which is certainly not a field.

Now, by assumption, $K[x_1,\ldots,x_n]$ is a field, so that it must contain the fraction field $K(x_1)$ of $K[x_1]$. Therefore it contains the ring $K(x_1)[x_2,\ldots,x_n]$. By induction, we may assume that $x_2,\ldots,x_n$ are algebraic over $K(x_1)$. (Note that even if K is algebraically closed, $K(x_1)$ is not a priori algebraically closed.) Thus we are reduced to proving that x_1 is algebraic over K.

Suppose that x_1 is transcendental over K. Since x_i, $i > 1$, is algebraic over $K(x_1)$ there is a polynomial $F(x_1)$ such that $F(x_1)x_i$ is integral over $K[x_1]$, (cf. ch. V, sect. 6) for all $i > 1$. From this it follows readily that if f is any element of $K[x_1,\ldots,x_n]$ then there is an integer r such that $F(x_1)^r f$ is integral over $K[x_1]$.

Since $K[x_1]$ is a unique factorization domain, it is integrally closed. This means that every element of $K(x_1)$ can be written in the form $G(x_1)/F(x_1)^r$ where $F,G \in K[x_1]$ and F is fixed. This is obviously absurd, so x_1 is algebraic over K.

I-2 AFFINE ALGEBRAIC SETS IN ABSTRACTO

We want to study the geometry on closed subsets of $\underline{A}^n$. However, it is evident that a closed set in $\underline{A}^n$ can be embedded as such in many different ways, e.g., if V is closed in $\underline{A}^n$ and T is an automorphism of $\underline{A}^n$ then TV is also closed in $\underline{A}^n$ and is certainly 'isomorphic' to V. These facts should indicate that the ambient space may be less valuable than it is troublesome in the study of geometry on V. In other words, in the context of a given problem, it may be desirable - even necessary - to consider an affine algebraic set independently of any ambient affine space. The price that is paid for this increase in abstraction is that, together with a particular affine algebraic set, we must consider all possible embeddings of that set into affine spaces. In fact, the mappings between affine algebraic sets assume a role that is at least as important as that played by the sets themselves. For this and other reasons, it becomes important to decide at the outset which such mappings we will regard as admissible. The key to this matter lies in translating the problem from a geometric one into an algebraic one, and for this purpose, the coordinate ring is the indispensible tool.

Now as we have already observed, if V is a closed subset of $\underline{A}^n$, then $k[V]$ is a homomorphic image of $k[\underline{A}^n]$. In particular, $k[V]$ is a finitely generated k-algebra without nilpotent elements. In fact, $k[V]$ is generated by the images $x_1,\ldots,x_n$ of $X_1,\ldots,X_n \in k[\underline{A}^n]$. On the other hand, suppose that we are given a finitely generated algebra R over k such that R is without nilpotent elements, then R is isomorphic to the coordinate ring of some closed set in $\underline{A}^n$, for a suitable (but not uniquely determined) n. We shall refer to such rings as <u>affine</u> <u>k-algebras</u>. If R is an affine k-algebra, and $f_1,\dots,f_n$ is a set of generators of R, then there is a surjective homomorphism from the polynomial ring $k[X_1,\dots,X_r]$ to R, obtained by sending f_i to X_i, $1 \leq i \leq r$. If I is the kernel of this homomorphism, then since R has no nilpotent elements, $F^n \in I$ implies $F \in I$, for all $F \in k[\underline{A}^r]$ and all $n > 0$. Therefore, by viii) of the exercise on p. 2, $I = \underline{I}(\underline{V}_{\underline{A}^r}(I))$, and R is isomorphic to $k[\underline{V}(I)]$. Thus any set of generators of R determines a closed set in affine space, whose coordinate ring is isomorphic to R.

DEFINITION 1.3. An <u>affine</u> <u>algebraic</u> <u>set</u> is a pair (V,R), where V is a set and R is an affine k-algebra of k-valued functions on V, such that:

i) If $\underline{m}$ is a maximal ideal of R then there is an $x \in V$ such that $\underline{m} = \{f \in R: f(x) = 0\}$.

ii) If $x \in V$, the set of $f \in R$ such that $f(x) = 0$ is a maximal ideal of R.

We may regard V as a topological space by taking the coarsest topology such that each $f \in R$, regarded as a mapping of V into $\underline{A}^1$, is continuous. This is the Zariski topology on V. As before, we can show that there is a basis for the closed sets consisting of sets of the form $\underline{V}_V(f) = \{x \in V: f(x) = 0\}$. Let us denote by V_f, for $f \in R$, the complement of $\underline{V}_V(f)$. Then a basis for the open sets is given by sets of the form V_f.

If (V,R) is an affine algebraic set, choose generators $f_1, \ldots, f_n$ for R and let V' be the closed set in $\underline{A}^n$ determined, as above, by these generators. We define a mapping $\varphi : V \to V'$ as follows. If $x \in V$, let $\underline{m}$ be the maximal ideal of functions in R which vanish at x. Then the inverse image, $\underline{m}'$ of $\underline{m}$ in $k[\underline{A}^n]$ is a maximal ideal. Let $\varphi(x) = x' = \underline{V}_{\underline{A}^n}(\underline{m}')$. Note that, by theorem A, $\underline{V}(\underline{m}') \neq \emptyset$. Moreover, if $\underline{V}(\underline{m}')$ contains more than one point then $\underline{m}'$ is not maximal, for if $x', x'' \in V(\underline{m}')$ and $x' \neq x''$, then there is an $F \in k[\underline{A}^n]$ such that $F(x') = 0$ and $F(x'') \neq 0$. Then $\underline{I}(\{x'\})$ is a proper ideal in $k[\underline{A}^n]$ and is larger than $\underline{m}'$. Now if $x' \in V'$, let $\underline{m}' = \underline{I}(\{x'\}) \subset k[\underline{A}^n]$. Since R is a homomorphic image of $k[\underline{A}^n]$, the image $\underline{m}$ of $\underline{m}'$ in R is maximal. Thus, by 1.3,i), there is an $x \in V$ such that $\underline{m}$

$= \{f \in R : f(x) = 0\}$. Let $\psi(x')$ be this x. By an argument similar to the one above - using 1.3.ii) - x is uniquely determined by x'. Then, as one readily sees, $\varphi \circ \psi$ is the identity on V and $\psi \circ \varphi$ is the identity on V'. Thus φ is bijective.

EXERCISE. Show that φ is a homeomorphism for the Zariski topologies on V and V' and that the mapping $\tilde{\varphi} : k[V] \to R$ given by $\tilde{\varphi}(f) = f \circ \varphi$ is a k-isomorphism of k-algebras.

The above argument shows that if (V,R) is an affine algebraic set, then the points of V are in natural bijective correspondence with the maximal ideals of R. If $\underline{M}(R)$ denotes the set of maximal ideals of R then we may transport the Zariski topology on V to $\underline{M}(R)$. Note that the basic open sets in $\underline{M}(R)$ are then of the form $\underline{M}(R)_f = \{\underline{m} \in \underline{M}(R) : f \notin \underline{m}\}$.

LEMMA 1.4. Let R be an affine k-algebra. If $\underline{m}$ is a maximal ideal of R then the field $R/\underline{m}$ is canonically isomorphic to k.

<u>Proof</u>: Since R is a homomorphic image of $k[\underline{A}^n]$ for some n, it suffices to prove the lemma for the latter ring. But by theorem A, and the above discussion, $\underline{V}(\underline{m}) \subset \underline{A}^n$ consists of a single point,

x, and the homomorphism $k[\underline{A}^n] \to k[\underline{A}^n]/\underline{m}$ is given by $F \mapsto F(x)$. Thus $k[\underline{A}^n]/\underline{m}$ is a subfield of k. But it contains k since reduction mod $\underline{m}$ is a k-homomorphism.

REMARK. Actually, lemma 1.4 is equivalent to the nullstellensatz (theorem A) and could be proved directly from Zariski's lemma. The lemma says that we can regard each $f \in R$ as a k-valued function on $\underline{M}(R)$, where $f(\underline{m}) = \underline{m}$-residue of f. This yields:

PROPOSITION 1.5. If R is an affine k-algebra, then $(\underline{M}(R), R)$ is an affine algebraic set.

Thus we have constructed a <u>canonical</u> affine algebraic set from a given affine k-algebra. Since this canonical "model" of the affine algebra obviously is independent of any ambient affine space, we have attained our first objective. It is quite clear that this model depends only on the ring R.

DEFINITION 1.6. If (V,R) is an affine algebraic set, we write k[V] for R and call this ring the <u>coordinate ring</u> of V. We will usually speak of V itself as an affine algebraic set.

DEFINITION 1.7. If V and V' are affine algebraic

sets, a mapping $\varphi: V \to V'$ is called a <u>k-morphism</u> if $f \in k[V']$ implies $f \circ \varphi \in k[V]$. We say that a k-morphism $\varphi: V \to V'$ is a k-isomorphism if it is bijective and φ^{-1} is a k-morphism.

If $\varphi: V \to V'$ is a k-morphism, then the mapping $f \mapsto f \circ \varphi$ of $k[V']$ into $k[V]$ is a homomorphism of k-algebras. This is because $1 \circ \varphi = 1$, $(f + g) \circ \varphi = (f \circ \varphi) + (g \circ \varphi)$, and $(fg) \circ \varphi = (f \circ \varphi)(g \circ \varphi)$. We denote this homomorphism by $\tilde{\varphi}$.

Conversely if $\eta: k[V'] \to k[V]$ is a homomorphism of k-algebras, we obtain a mapping $\tilde{\eta}$ from V to V' as follows. If $x \in V$, let $\underline{m}$ be the corresponding maximal ideal in $k[V]$. Then the inverse image of $\underline{m}$ in $k[V']$ is a maximal ideal. This follows from:

LEMMA 1.8. If R and R' are affine k-algebras and $\eta: R' \to R$ is a k-algebra homomorphism, then if $\underline{m}$ is a maximal ideal of R, $\underline{m} = \eta^{-1}\underline{m}$ is a maximal ideal of R'.

<u>Proof</u>: That $\underline{m}'$ is an ideal is evident. By the homomorphism theorems, η induces an injection $R'/\underline{m}' \to R/\underline{m}$ which is itself a k-algebra homomorphism. Since k is naturally a subring of $R'/\underline{m}'$ it follows that the induced homomorphism is an isomorphism, viz., $k \subset$ (image of $R'/\underline{m}'$) $\subset R/\underline{m} \subset k$. Thus $R'/\underline{m}'$ is a field and $\underline{m}'$ is maximal.

Now returning to the previous discussion, let $\underline{m}'$ determine the point $x' \in V'$ and let $\tilde{\eta}(x) = x'$. Then if $f \in k[V']$ and $x \in V$, we have $(f \circ \tilde{\eta})(x) = \eta(f)(x)$ so $\tilde{\tilde{\eta}} = \eta$, and $\tilde{\eta}$ is a k-morphism. In other words, a k-morphism $\varphi : V \to V'$ determines, and is determined by, the k-algebra homomorphism $\tilde{\varphi} : k[V'] \to k[V]$, viz., $\tilde{\tilde{\varphi}} = \varphi$. Furthermore, if

$$V \xrightarrow{\varphi'} V' \xrightarrow{\varphi''} V''$$

are k-morphisms, then $\widetilde{\varphi'' \circ \varphi'} = \tilde{\varphi}' \circ \tilde{\varphi}''$, and if

$$k[V] \xrightarrow{\eta'} k[V'] \xrightarrow{\eta''} k[V'']$$

are k-algebra homomorphisms, then $\widetilde{\eta'' \circ \eta'} = \tilde{\eta}' \circ \tilde{\eta}''$.

REMARK. The correct context for this correspondence between affine algebraic sets and their coordinate rings is that of categories. In that language, the correspondence $V \mapsto k[V]$ is a functor which sets up an equivalence between the category of affine algebraic sets and k-morphisms and the category of affine k-algebras and k-algebra homomorphisms. This 'duality' provides a useful tool in the study of the geometry on V or - what is the same thing - the algebra of $k[V]$.

I-3 NOETHERIAN RINGS

Even though most readers will be familiar with the material in this section, nevertheless we shall prove those results which we make use of later. It is of more than passing interest to note that the origins of the theory of noetherian rings can be found in Hilbert's work on invariant theory. In fact, the Hilbert basis theorem (1.12 below) was the critical lemma in his solution of the classical finiteness problem.

DEFINITION 1.9. Let R be a commutative ring with identity and let M be an R-module. We say that M satisfies the ascending chain condition (a.c.c.) if every ascending chain, $M_1 \subset M_2 \subset M_3 \subset \cdots$ of R-submodules of M has the property that $M_i = M_{i+1}$ for sufficiently large i.

LEMMA 1.10. Every R-submodule of the R-module M is finitely generated if and only if M satisfies the ascending chain condition.

Proof: Recall first that an R-module N is said to be finitely generated if there exist elements $n_1, \ldots, n_t \in N$, such that every element of N is of the form $\sum r_i n_i$ for suitable $r_i \in R$.

To prove the lemma, assume first that every submodule of M is finitely generated. If $M_1 \subset M_2 \subset \cdots$ is an ascending chain of submodules, let $N = \bigcup_i M_i$. Then N is a submodule. If $m_1, \ldots, m_t$ generate N, and $m_j \in M_{p_j}$, let $p_o =$

$\max(p_j)$. Then $N \subset M_{p_o}$ so $M_i = M_{i+1}$ for $i > p_o$. Conversely, suppose that M satisfies the a.c.c., and let N be a submodule of M requiring infinitely many generators, m_s, $s \in S$. Then one can find a sequence of subsets, $S_1 < S_2 < S_3 < \cdots$ of S such that if M_j is the submodule generated by $\{m_s : s \in S_j\}$, then $M_1 < M_2 < M_3 < \cdots$ is a strictly ascending chain of submodules, contradicting the a.c.c.

DEFINITION 1.11. A commutative ring with identity is called a <u>noetherian</u> <u>ring</u> if it satisfies the ascending chain condition for submodules of itself, i.e., ideals. This is equivalent - by 1.10 - to the condition that every ideal be finitely generated.

THEOREM 1.12. If R is a noetherian ring, then the ring $R[X]$ of polynomials in the variable X with coefficients in R is also noetherian.

<u>Proof</u>: We show that $R[X]$ satisfies the ascending chain condition for ideals. If $I_1 \subset I_2 \subset I_3 \subset \cdots$ is an ascending chain of ideals in $R[X]$, let L_{ij} be the set of leading coefficients of elements of degree i in I_j - together with 0. A simple argument, which we shall omit, shows that L_{ij} is an ideal in R, and that $L_{i,j-1} \subset L_{ij}$ and $L_{i-1,j} \subset L_{ij}$, for all i and j. In fact, one can prove that

if $L_{i,j+1} = L_{ij}$ for all i, then $I_j = I_{j+1}$. Admitting this last assertion for the moment, let L_{pq} be a maximal element of the double sequence (L_{ij}) - which exists by the chain condition on R. Then $L_{pq} = L_{ij}$ if $i \geqslant p$ and $j \geqslant q$. For fixed i, the sequence (L_{ij}) terminates - say at L_{i,n_i}. Then if $i \geqslant p$, it follows that $n_i \leqslant q$. Since the number of i's less than or equal to p is finite, the number of n_i's greater than or equal to q is finite. Choose an $n > n_i$ for all i. Then $L_{ij} = L_{in}$ for every i and every $j \geqslant n$. Thus $I_j = I_n$ whenever $j \geqslant n$.

The previous argument is completely formal. To complete the proof, we must verify the unproved assertion above. Suppose that $g \in I_{j+1}$ has degree i. Since $L_{ij} = L_{i,j+1}$, there is an $f \in I_j$ having the same leading term as g. Then $f - g$ has degree $\leqslant i - 1$. Repeating the argument, we obtain polynomials $f = f_i, f_{i+1}, \ldots, f_{i+p} \in I_j$ such that the polynomial,

$$g - \sum_{k=0}^{p} f_{i+k} ,$$

has degree $\leqslant i - p - 1$. When $p = i$, this polynomial must be 0, so that $g \in I_j$. q.e.d.

COROLLARY 1.13. If R is noetherian, then the ring $R[X_1, \ldots, X_n]$ of polynomials in the variables $X_1, \ldots, X_n$ with coefficients in R is noetherian.

Proof: Apply induction, noting that $R[X_1,\ldots,X_n] = R[X_1,\ldots,X_{n-1}][X_n]$.

COROLLARY 1.14. If R is noetherian, then any finitely generated R-algebra is noetherian.

Proof: It is obvious from the definition that a homomorphic image of a noetherian ring is noetherian.

COROLLARY 1.15. An affine k-algebra is noetherian.

COROLLARY 1.16. If V is an affine algebraic set and $Z_1 > Z_2 > Z_3 > \cdots$ is a descending chain of closed subsets of V, then $Z_i = Z_{i+1}$ for i large.

EXERCISE: Prove corollary 1.16.

PROPOSITION 1.17. If R is noetherian ring and M is an R-module, then M is finitely generated if and only if M satisfies the a.c.c.

Proof: If M satisfies the a.c.c., then M is finitely generated by lemma 1.10. Conversely, if $m_1,\ldots,m_n$ generate M, then the R-module homomorphism $R^n \longrightarrow M$ which sends $(0,\ldots,\overset{i}{1},\ldots,0)$ to m_i is surjective. Hence it suffices to show that R^n satisfies the a.c.c., as a homomorphic image of an a.c.c. module is obviously an a.c.c. module.

The result then follows by an easy induction from:

LEMMA 1.18. Let R be a commutative ring with identity. Let M be an R-module and let N be an R-submodule of M. If N and M/N satisfy the a.c.c., then M satisfies the a.c.c.

<u>Proof</u>: We leave to the reader to verify that if L and L' are submodules of M such that $L + N = L' + N$ and $L \cap N = L' \cap N$, then $L = L'$. By the homomorphism theorems and the a.c.c. in N and M/N, if $L_1 \subset L_2 \subset L_3 \subset \cdots$ is an ascending chain of submodules of M, then $L_j + N = L_{j+1} + N$ and $L_j \cap N = L_{j+1} \cap N$ for j large. Thus $L_j = L_{j+1}$ for j large.

WARNING: The notions of finite generation for R-modules and of finite generation for R-algebras are quite different. An R-algebra S is a finitely generated R-algebra if there is a surjective R-algebra homomorphism $R[X_1,\ldots,X_n] \to S$, for some n. An R-module M is a finitely generated R-module if there is a surjective R-module homomorphism $R^n \to M$, for some n. In the former case the homomorphism must be a ring homomorphism, and in the latter it need only be a module homomorphism. In any case, $R[X_1,\ldots,X_n]$ is much 'bigger' than R^n. Thus, e.g., the polynomial ring $k[X]$ is a finitely generated k-algebra but is not a finitely generated k-module, i.e., is not a finite dimensional vector space over k.

I-4 DECOMPOSITION OF AFFINE ALGEBRAIC SETS

DEFINITION 1.19. If T is a topological space, T is said to be irreducible if any two non-empty open sets in T have non-empty intersection. This is equivalent to requiring that T not be the union of two proper closed subsets.

DEFINITION 1.20. If X is a set, and S_i, $i \in I$ are subsets of X, we say that the union $\bigcup_i S_i$ is irredundant if $S_i \subset S_j$ implies $i = j$.

PROPOSITION 1.21. Every affine algebraic set is a finite irredundant union of irreducible closed subsets. This decomposition is unique, i.e., any two such decompositions involve the same irreducible closed subsets.

Proof: If the first assertion is false for V, then $V = W_1 \cup W_1'$, with W_1 and W_1' proper closed subsets. Then the assertion must be false for one of W_1 or W_1' - say for W_1. Then $W_1 = W_2 \cup W_2'$, with W_2 and W_2' proper closed subsets of W_1, etc. Repetition of the argument yields an infinite strictly descending sequence $W_1 > W_2 > W_3 > \cdots$ of closed subsets of V, contradicting corollary 1.16. Thus

$$V = \bigcup_{i=1}^{n} V_i ,$$

with each V_i closed and irreducible. Throwing away superfluous terms gives an irredundant union.

Now for uniqueness, suppose that

$$V = \bigcup_{i=1}^{m} W_i$$

is another irredundant decomposition with W_i irreducible. Then $V_1 \subset \bigcup W_i$ implies $V_1 = \bigcup (W_i \cap V_1)$ so that $V_1 \subset W_i$ for some i. By a similar argument, we see that $W_i \subset V_j$ for some j. Then $V_1 \subset W_i \subset V_j$, whence $V_1 = W_i = V_j$. Now repeat the argument for V_2, etc.

PROPOSITION 1.22. If V is an affine algebraic set, then V is irreducible if and only if k[V] has no zero-divisors $\neq 0$.

Proof: If $f,g \in k[V]$, and $f \neq 0 \neq g$, then $\underline{V}(f)$ and $\underline{V}(g)$ are proper closed subsets of V, and if $fg = 0$, then $V = \underline{V}(fg) = \underline{V}(f) \cup \underline{V}(g)$. Thus V irreducible implies k[V] has no proper zero-divisors. Conversely, if $V = V' \cup V''$, with V' and V'' proper closed subsets of V, let $I' = \{f \in k[V] : f|V' = 0\}$, $I'' = \{f \in k[V] : f|V'' = 0\}$. Then neither I' nor I'' is the zero ideal, but $I' \cap I'' = (0)$. Hence k[V] has proper zero-divisors.

We shall carry over the $\underline{V}$, $\underline{I}$ notation from $(\underline{A}^n, k[\underline{A}^n])$ to arbitrary affine algebraic sets. We leave it to the reader to prove the analogue of the exercise on p.2.

DEFINITION 1.23. An irreducible affine algebraic set is called an affine variety. The affine varieties occurring in the decomposition of an affine algebraic set V are called the irreducible components of V.

I-5 PRODUCTS OF AFFINE ALGEBRAIC SETS

We digress briefly to recall the notion of the tensor product of modules. Let R be a commutative ring with identity and let M and N be R-modules. Let P be the free abelian group on the set M x N, and let Q be the subgroup generated by all elements of P of the form

$$(rm,n) - (m,rn) \qquad m \in M,\ n \in N,\ r \in R,$$

$$(m+m',n) - (m,n) - (m',n) \quad m,m' \in M,\ n \in N,$$

$$(m,n+n') - (m,n) - (m,n') \quad m \in M,\ n,n' \in N.$$

Set $M \otimes_R N = P/Q$ and call this group the tensor product of M and N over R. Let $m \otimes n$ denote the image of (m,n) in $M \otimes_R N$, and make $M \otimes_R N$ into an R-module by defining $r(m \otimes n) = rm \otimes n$ $(= m \otimes rn)$. It is easy to check that this does give an R-module structure.

EXERCISE. Show that the tensor product $M \otimes_R N$ is characterized by the following universal mapping property.

> If L is an R-module, and $f: M \times N \to L$ is a mapping such that
>
> $f(rm + r'm', n) = rf(m,n) + r'f(m',n)$
>
> $f(m, rn + r'n') = rf(m,n) + r'f(m,n')$
>
> $f(rm,n) = f(m,rn)$,
>
> for all $m, m' \in M$, $n, n' \in N$ and $r, r' \in R$, then there is a unique R-module homomorphism $\varphi: M \otimes_R N \to L$ such that $\varphi(m \otimes n) = f(m,n)$ for all $m \in M$, $n \in N$.

Show also that if $\eta: M \to M'$ and $\vartheta: N \to N'$ are R-module homomorphisms, then there is a unique R-module homomorphism - which we denote by $\eta \otimes \vartheta$ - from $M \otimes_R N$ to $M' \otimes_R N'$ taking $m \otimes n$ to $\eta m \otimes \vartheta n$. Finally, show that if S and T are R-algebras, then there is a unique R-algebra structure on $S \otimes_R T$ such that $(s \otimes t)(s' \otimes t') = ss' \otimes tt'$.

Now suppose that $V \subset \underline{A}^n$ and $W \subset \underline{A}^m$ are closed subsets. Let $p = n + m$. Then $V \times W$ is a subset of $\underline{A}^n \times \underline{A}^m = \underline{A}^p$. If $I = \underline{I}_{\underline{A}^n}(V)$ and $J = \underline{I}_{\underline{A}^m}(W)$, we identify $k[\underline{A}^n] = k[X_1,\ldots,X_n]$ and $k[\underline{A}^m] = k[Y_1,\ldots,Y_m]$ as subrings of $k[\underline{A}^p] = k[X_1,\ldots,X_n,Y_1,\ldots,Y_m]$, and let (I,J) be the ideal in $k[\underline{A}^p]$ generated by $I \cup J$.

PROPOSITION 1.24. $V \times W = \underline{V}_{\underline{A}^p}((I,J))$.

Proof: If $H(X,Y) \in (I,J)$, then

$$H(X,Y) = \sum_i H_i(X,Y)F_i(X) + K_i(X,Y)G_i(Y),$$

where $F_i \in I$, $G_i \in J$, and $H_i, K_i \in k[\underline{A}^p]$. Now if $(v,w) \in V \times W$, then

$$H(v,w) = \sum_i H_i(v,w)F_i(v) + K_i(v,w)G_i(w) = 0,$$

so that $(v,w) \in \underline{V}_{\underline{A}^p}((I,J))$. Conversely, if $(x,y) \notin V \times W$, say $x \notin V$. Then there is an $F \in I$ such that $F(x) \neq 0$. But F - regarded as an element of $k[\underline{A}^p]$,- lies in (I,J) and $F(x,y) = F(x) \neq 0$.

While it is quite easy to show that $V \times W = \underline{V}((I,J))$, it is somewhat harder to prove that $(I,J) = \underline{I}(V \times W)$. This fact will come out of the solution of the following problem: to describe $k[V \times W]$ without referring to particular affine embeddings of V and W. In other words, what operation on affine k-algebras corresponds to the product of affine algebraic sets? The answer is provided by the tensor product. To prove this, we must digress again.

If M, N, and P are abelian groups, we say that the sequence of homomorphisms

$$M \xrightarrow{\eta} N \xrightarrow{\vartheta} P$$

is <u>exact</u> at N if $\ker\vartheta = \operatorname{image}\eta$. In general, we say that a sequence of homomorphisms

$$\cdots \to M_i \to M_{i+1} \to M_{i+2} \to \cdots$$

is exact if it is exact at each M_i. In particular, the sequence

$$0 \to M \xrightarrow{\eta} N \xrightarrow{\vartheta} P \to 0$$

is exact if η is injective, ϑ surjective and $\ker\vartheta = \operatorname{image}\eta$

LEMMA 1.25. If R is a commutative ring with identity and

$$0 \to M \xrightarrow{\varphi} N \xrightarrow{\psi} P \to 0$$

is an exact sequence of R-modules and R-module homomorphisms, then for any R-module Q the sequence

$$M \otimes_R Q \xrightarrow{\varphi\otimes 1} N \otimes_R Q \xrightarrow{\psi\otimes 1} P \otimes_R Q \to 0$$

is exact.

<u>Proof</u>: Since $(\psi \otimes 1)(\varphi \otimes 1) = \psi\circ\varphi \otimes 1$, it follows that $(\psi \otimes 1)(\varphi \otimes 1) = 0$. Thus there is a homomorphism, $\eta : (N \otimes Q)/(\varphi\otimes 1)(M\otimes Q) \to P\otimes Q$. To show that η is bijective, define a homomorphism α : $P\otimes Q \to (N\otimes Q)/(\varphi\otimes 1)(M\otimes Q)$ as follows. Given $p \in P$, $q \in Q$, choose $n \in N$ such that $\psi n = p$. Let $\underline{\alpha}(p,q)$ = class of $n\otimes q$ modulo $(\varphi\otimes 1)(M\otimes Q)$. Clearly $\underline{\alpha}$ satisfies the hypotheses of the universal mapping property of tensor products, so we can let α be the homomorphism induced by $\underline{\alpha}$. As

$\alpha \circ \eta$ is the identity on $N \otimes Q/(\varphi \otimes 1)M \otimes Q$ and $\eta \circ \alpha$ is the identity on $P \otimes Q$, we are done.

COMPLEMENT 1.26. If $R = K$ is a field, then $\varphi \otimes 1$ is injective, i.e., the sequence

$$0 \to M \otimes Q \to N \otimes Q \to P \otimes Q \to 0$$

is exact.

Proof: Fix a basis (p_i) for P and choose n_i N such that $\psi n_i = p_i$. Let $\underline{\alpha} p_i = n_i$. Since P is a vector space, $\underline{\alpha}$ defines a homomorphism α: $P \to N$ such that $\psi \circ \alpha$ is the identity on P. Thus $N = (\operatorname{im} \alpha) \oplus \varphi M$, with $\operatorname{im} \alpha$ isomorphic to P. But $\varphi : M \to \varphi M$ is an isomorphism and $N \otimes Q = (\operatorname{im} \alpha \otimes Q) \oplus (\varphi M \otimes Q)$. Thus $\varphi \otimes 1 : M \otimes Q \to \varphi M \otimes Q$ is an isomorphism and $\varphi M \otimes Q = \ker(\psi \otimes 1)$.

LEMMA 1.27. If M, M' and N, N' are R-modules and $\varphi : N' \to N$, $\psi : M' \to M$ are R-module homomorphisms, then the R-modules

$$(M \otimes_R N)/[(\psi \otimes 1)(M' \otimes_R N) + (1 \otimes \psi)(M \otimes_R N')]$$

and

$$(M/\psi M') \otimes_R (N/\varphi N')$$

are canonically isomorphic.

Proof: Lemma 1.25, together with the homomorphism theorems, shows that the rows and columns of the following diagram of homomorphisms are exact. The diagram is also 'commutative' in the sense that any two paths with the same start and finish represent the same mapping.

$$
\begin{array}{ccccccc}
0 & & 0 & & 0 & & \\
\uparrow & & \uparrow & & \uparrow & & \\
M'\otimes_R (N/\varphi N') & \xrightarrow{\gamma} & M\otimes_R (N/\varphi N') & \xrightarrow{\alpha} & (M/\psi M')\otimes_R (N/\varphi N') & \rightarrow & 0 \\
\delta \uparrow & & \beta \uparrow & \overset{\varphi}{\nearrow} & \uparrow & & \\
M'\otimes_R N & \xrightarrow{\vartheta} & M\otimes_R N & \longrightarrow & (M/\psi M')\otimes_R N & \rightarrow & 0 \\
\uparrow & & \eta \uparrow & & \uparrow & & \\
M'\otimes_R N' & \longrightarrow & M\otimes_R N' & \longrightarrow & (M/\psi M')\otimes_R N' & \rightarrow & 0
\end{array}
$$

φ is defined as $\alpha \circ \beta$. If $\varphi x = 0$, then $\beta x = \gamma y$ for some y, and $y = \delta z$ for some z, i.e., $\beta x = \gamma\delta z$. Thus $x = \vartheta z \pmod{\eta(M\otimes N')}$, i.e., $x \in \vartheta(M'\otimes N) + \eta(M\otimes N')$.

COMPLEMENT 1.28. If $R = K$ is a field and if $M' \subset M$ and $N' \subset N$, then identifying $M'\otimes N$ and $M\otimes N'$ as subspaces of $M\otimes N$, there is a canonical isomorphism between $(M/M')\otimes(N/N')$ and $M\otimes N/M'\otimes N + M\otimes N'$.

EXERCISE. Show that the mapping $X_i \otimes 1 \mapsto X_i$, $1\otimes Y_j \mapsto Y_j$ induces a k-algebra isomorphism

$$k[X_1,\ldots,X_n] \otimes_k k[Y_1,\ldots,Y_m] \approx k[X_1,\ldots,X_n,Y_1,\ldots,Y_m]$$

PROPOSITION 1.29. If $I \subset k[\underline{A}^n]$ and $J \subset k[\underline{A}^m]$ are ideals, then $(k[\underline{A}^n]/I) \otimes (k[\underline{A}^m]/J)$ is isomorphic as k-algebra to $k[\underline{A}^p]/(I,J)$, $p = n + m$.

Proof: In complement 1.28, take $N = k[\underline{A}^n]$, $N' = I$, $M = k[\underline{A}^m]$, $M' = J$. By the exercise, $N \otimes M$ is isomorphic to $k[\underline{A}^p]$. The complement yields an isomorphism

$$(k[\underline{A}^n]/I) \otimes (k[\underline{A}^m]/J) \approx k[\underline{A}^p]/(I \otimes k[\underline{A}^m] + k[\underline{A}^n] \otimes J)$$

of k-vector spaces. It is readily checked that this is a k-algebra isomorphism. It only remains to verify the identification of $I \otimes k[\underline{A}^m] + k[\underline{A}^n] \otimes J$ with (I,J). Using the isomorphism of the exercise, we see that $F \otimes G + H \otimes K$ is mapped to $FG + HK$. Now if $H(X,Y) = \sum H_i(X,Y)F_i(X) + K_i(X,Y)G_i(Y)$, with $F_i \in I$, $G_i \in J$ and $H_i, K_i \in k[\underline{A}^p]$, we write $H_i(X,Y) = \sum_j H'_{ij}(X)H''_{ij}(Y)$, $K_i(X,Y) = \sum_j K'_{ij}(X)K''_{ij}(Y)$. Then

$$H(X,Y) = \sum_i (\sum_j H''_{ij}(Y)F'_{ij}(X) + \sum_j K'_{ij}(X)G'_{ij}(Y)),$$

where $F'_{ij} \in I$, $G'_{ij} \in J$.

If we can show that $(I,J) = \underline{I}_{\underline{A}^p}(V \times W)$, where $I = \underline{I}_{\underline{A}^n}(V)$ and $J = \underline{I}_{\underline{A}^m}(W)$, $p = n + m$, then we will have shown that the coordinate ring of $V \times W$ is canonically isomorphic to $k[V] \otimes k[W]$, yielding an intrinsic description of the product of two affine algebraic sets. For this, however, it evidently suffices to prove:

PROPOSITION 1.30. If R and S are affine k-algebras, then $R \otimes_k S$ is an affine k-algebra.

Proof: If $R = k[V]$ and $S = k[W]$, then there is a surjective k-algebra homomorphism $\varphi : R \otimes S \to k[V \times W]$ given by $(\varphi(\sum f_i \otimes g_i))(x,y) = \sum f_i(x)g_i(y)$ Therefore, by the nullstellensatz, it suffices to show that if $f \in R \otimes S$ has the property that φf vanishes at all points of $V \times W$, then $f = 0$. Write $f = \sum f_i \otimes g_i$, with $f_i \in R$, $g_i \in S$. Choose such an expression for f involving the least number of non-zero f_i. If $f \neq 0$, then the g_i cannot all be 0. Then there is a point y of W such that not all $g_i(y)$ are 0. Since $\sum f_i(x)g_i(y) = 0$ for all $x \in V$, the f_i are linearly dependent over k. Thus we can write $f_1 = \sum_{i>1} a_i f_i$, $a_i \in k$. Then

$$\begin{aligned} f &= f_1 \otimes g_1 + \sum_{i>1} f_i \otimes g_i \\ &= \sum_{i>1} (a_i f_i \otimes g_1 + f_i \otimes g_i) \\ &= \sum_{i>1} (f_i \otimes a_i g_1 + f_i \otimes g_i) \\ &= \sum_{i>1} f_i \otimes (a_i g_1 + g_i). \end{aligned}$$

The last expression involves fewer non-zero f_i's so that $f = 0$.

There is one more point about products that should be settled. Is the product of affine varieties an affine variety? This can be proved by hard algebra or by the following simple topological argument.

PROPOSITION 1.31. If V and W are affine varieties, then so is $V \times W$.

Proof: It suffices to show that $V \times W$ is irreducible. For each $y \in W$, $V \times \{y\}$ is k-isomorphic to V and hence irreducible. Now if $V \times W = Z \cup Z'$ with Z and Z' closed, then for each $y \in W$, we have

$$V \times \{y\} = (Z \cap (V \times \{y\})) \cup (Z' \cap (V \times \{y\}))$$

so that either $V \times \{y\} \subset Z$ or $V \times \{y\} \subset Z'$. Now let $W_1 = \{y \in W : V \times \{y\} \subset Z\}$ and $W_2 = \{y \in W : V \times \{y\} \subset Z'\}$. Then $W = W_1 \cup W_2$. If $x \in V$, then the canonical isomorphism of W with $\{x\} \times W$ maps W_1 onto $Z \cap (\{x\} \times W)$ and W_2 onto $Z' \cap (\{x\} \times W)$. Therefore W_1 and W_2 are closed in W. Thus either $W_1 = W$ or $W_2 = W$ so that either $V \times W = Z$ or $V \times W = Z'$. Thus $V \times W$ is irreducible.

I-6 EXAMPLES OF AFFINE ALGEBRAIC SETS

Aside from the "easy" examples of hypersurfaces in $\underline{A}^n$, it may not be a trivial matter to prove that a given subset of $\underline{A}^n$ is closed. The only general method for doing this is to produce a defining ideal in $k[\underline{A}^n]$. For instance, take the familiar 'twisted cubic' curve in $\underline{A}^3$. This curve can be obtained by intersecting two quadric surfaces with a common line and removing the line. If X, Y, Z are coordinates in $\underline{A}^3$, we may assume that the line is given by $Y = Z = 0$. Let Q_1 be the quadric cone defined by $XZ - Y^2$ and Q_2 the cylinder defined by $Y - Z^2$. Then the ideal of $Q_1 \cap Q_2$ is generated by $XZ - Y^2$ and $Y - Z^2$. Since $Q_1 \cap Q_2 = L \cup C$, where L is the given line and C is the twisted cubic, we have $(XZ - Y^2, Y - Z^2) = (Y,Z) \cap I$, where I is the ideal of C. Solving residually, we have $xz = z^4$, or $x = z^3 = yz$. From this we see that $I = (XZ - Y^2, Y - Z^2, X - YZ)$. Thus, even though C is a curve in 3-space, three equations and not two are required to define it.

EXERCISE. Show that any curve in $\underline{A}^3$ can be defined by at most three equations.

It is worth noting that the Zariski topology on the product of two affine algebraic sets may not coincide with the product topology. For example, consider $\underline{A}^2 = \underline{A}^1 \times \underline{A}^1$. If X and Y are coordinates here, then the line defined by $X - Y$ is not closed in the product topology. The subbasic closed sets in the product topology are lines "parallel to the axes". Since these sets are closed in the Zariski topology, it follows that closed sets in the product topology are closed in the Zariski topology. By corollary 1.16, we see that the given line must be a <u>finite</u> intersection of sets which are finite unions of the above subbasic lines. This is evidently absurd.

One might ask whether an open subset of an affine algebraic set is itself an affine algebraic set. The answer in general is negative, but the next proposition shows that this is so for "small" open sets.

PROPOSITION 1.32. Let V be an affine algebraic set and let f be a non-zero element of $k[V]$. Let $V_f = \{x \in V : f(x) \neq 0\}$. Let R_o be the ring whose elements are the restrictions of elements of $k[V]$ to V_f. Let $1/f$ denote the function on V_f defined by $(1/f)(x) = 1/f(x)$, and let $R = R_o[1/f]$ Then (V_f, R) is an affine algebraic set.

<u>Proof</u>: Clearly R is an affine k-algebra of k-valued functions on V_f. It suffices to show that

maximal ideals of R correspond to points of V_f in the manner of definition 1.3. If $x \in V_f$, let $\underline{m} = \{g \in R ; g(x) = 0\}$. Then $\underline{m} \cap R_o$ is clearly a maximal ideal of R_o, and by lemma 1.4, $R_o/\underline{m} \cap R_o = k$. Since the image of f in $R/\underline{m}$ lies in k and is not 0, the image of $1/f$ in $R/\underline{m}$ lies in k. Thus $R/\underline{m} = k$, and $\underline{m}$ is maximal.

Now given a maximal ideal $\underline{m}$ of R, we know from lemma 1.8 that the inverse image $\underline{n}$ of $\underline{m}$ in $k[V]$ is a maximal ideal in $k[V]$. Let x be the corresponding point of V. Since f is clearly not in $\underline{n}$, it follows that $x \in V_f$. I claim that $\underline{n}R = \underline{m}$. To prove this we may assume that $R_o = k[V]$. Each element of R is of the form g/f^n, $g \in R_o$. Thus, given $g \in \underline{m}$, we have $f^n g \in \underline{n}$ for a suitable n. This proves our claim and the proposition.

REMARK. Note that the proof of proposition 1.32 shows that if V can be embedded in $\underline{A}^n$ then V_f can be embedded in $\underline{A}^{n+1}$.

There is one example, which because of its importance for invariant theory, should be discussed here. Suppose that V is an affine algebraic set. The ordered n-tuples of points of V are just the points of $V^n = V \times \cdots \times V$ (n factors). One may then ask whether the unordered n-tuples of points of V form an affine algebraic set. We shall see that this is indeed the case in chapter V. For the present, we shall simply give a direct proof of this fact in the case where $V = \underline{A}^1$.

The above problem may be restated as follows. The symmetric group S_n of degree n acts on the points of V^n by permuting the factors. Is there an affine algebraic set V_o and a k-morphism $\pi : V \to V_o$ such that for each $y \in V_o$, $\pi^{-1}(y)$ consists of exactly one orbit of the action of S_n on V^n ? This means that V_o is the "space of orbits" for the action of S_n on V^n.

Suppose that such a V_o does exist. What is its coordinate ring ? Each $s \in S_n$ induces a k-automorphism of V, denoted by $v \mapsto sv$. This induces, in turn, an automorphism of $k[V]$, viz., $f \mapsto f^s$, where $f^s(v) = f(sv)$. An element of $k[V^n]$ induces a function on V_o if it is constant on the orbits of S_n. Conversely, an element of $k[V_o]$ induces a function on V^n which is constant on orbits. Since π is surjective, $\widetilde{\pi} : k[V_o] \to k[V^n]$ is injective, so that $k[V_o]$ can be identified with the subring of $k[V^n]$ consisting of elements invariant under S_n, i.e., those f such that $f^s = f$, for all $s \in S_n$. We denote this ring by $k[V^n]^{S_n}$.

Suppose now that $k[V^n]^{S_n}$ is an affine k-algebra. Let V_o be the affine algebraic set corresponding to this ring and let π be the k-morphism from V^n to V_o corresponding to the inclusion of $k[V^n]^{S_n}$ in $k[V^n]$. Since invariants are clearly constant on orbits, one sees immediately that each orbit in V^n is mapped to a point in V_o. To show that distinct orbits go to distinct points of V_o it suffices to show that if z and z' are points of V^n in different orbits, then there is an invariant f in $k[V^n]$ such that $f(z) \neq f(z')$. Let us write $z = v_1 + v_2 + \ldots + v_n$, $z' = v_1' + v_2' + \ldots + v_n'$. Then we may assume that $v_1 \neq v_1'$. Then there is an $f_1 \in k[V]$ such that $f_1(v_1) = 0$, $f_1(v_1') = 1$. Now choose $f_i \in k[V]$, $2 \leq i \leq n$, such that $f_i(v_i) = f_i(v_i') = 1$. Let $f = f_1 \otimes f_2 \otimes \ldots \otimes f_n \in k[V^n] = k[V] \otimes \ldots \otimes k[V]$ (n factors). Clearly f is invariant and $f(z) = 0$, $f(z') = 1$.

We will then be finished with our construction if we can show that $k[V^n]^{S_n}$ is an affine k-algebra. Since $k[V^n]$ has no nilpotent elements, it suffices to prove that $k[V^n]^{S_n}$ is finitely generated. In the case where $V = \underline{A}^1$, we have a very explicit description of the ring of invariants.

We define the j-th elementary symmetric function of $X_1, \ldots, X_n$ by

$$E_j(X_1, \ldots, X_n) = \sum X_{i_1} \cdots X_{i_j}$$

where the sum is taken over all j element subsets

of $\{1,\ldots,n\}$. Thus, e.g., $E_2(X_1,X_2,X_3) = X_1X_2 + X_2X_3 + X_1X_3$. Let us also denote $E_p(X_1,\ldots,X_q)$ by $E_{p,q}$. Note that the action of S_n on $k[\underline{A}^n]$ is given by $F^s(X_1,\ldots,X_n) = F(X_{s(1)},\ldots,X_{s(n)})$. Then we have

PROPOSITION 1.33. $k[\underline{A}^n]^{S_n} = k[E_{1,n},\ldots,E_{n,n}]$.

<u>Proof</u>: The proposition being trivial for n = 1, we use induction on n. Set $R_n = k[\underline{A}^n]^{S_n}$. We use an auxiliary induction on the degree of $F \in R_n$ to show that it is a polynomial in $E_{1,n},\ldots,E_{n,n}$. If F has degree 1, then $F = b + a_1X_1 + \ldots + a_nX_n$ and we must have $a_i = a_j$ so that $F = b + aE_{1,n}$. If F has degree p, assume that all invariants of degree less than p are polynomials in $E_{1,n},\ldots,E_{n,n}$. Write $F = f_o + f_1X_n + \ldots + f_pX_n^p$, where the f_i are elements of $k[X_1,\ldots,X_{n-1}]$. Applying permutations leaving X_n fixed, we see that $f_i \in R_{n-1}$, $0 \leqslant i \leqslant p$, so that each f_i is a polynomial in $E_{1,n-1},\ldots,E_{n-1,n-1}$.

Next we note that $E_{j,n} = E_{j,n-1} + X_nE_{j-1,n-1}$. We have $F = f_o + X_nf$, $f_o \in R_{n-1}$, $f \in k[\underline{A}^n]$, and we can write $f_o = g_o(E_{1,n-1},\ldots,E_{n-1,n-1})$. Also

$$g_o(E_{1,n},\ldots,E_{n-1,n}) = g_o(E_{1,n-1},\ldots,E_{n-1,n-1}) + X_nh(X_1,\ldots,X_n).$$

Thus $F(X_1,\ldots,X_n) = g_o(E_{1,n},\ldots,E_{n-1,n}) + X_n(f - h)$.

Note that $g_o(E_{1,n},\dots,E_{n-1,n})$ and $g_o(E_{1,n-1},\dots,E_{n-1,n-1})$ have the same degree which is $< p$. Since F and $g_o(E_{1,n},\dots,E_{n-1,n})$ are invariant, it follows that $X_n(f - h)$ is invariant, and hence that $X_1X_2\cdots X_{n-1}$ divides $f - h$. Thus

$$F - g_o(E_{1,n},\dots,E_{n-1,n}) = E_{n,n}H(X_1,\dots,X_n).$$

Since H must be invariant and of degree $< p$, the proposition is proved.

As a final touch, we show that the ring $R_n = k[E_{1,n},\dots,E_{n,n}]$ is isomorphic to $k[\underline{A}^n]$. To see this, map $k[\underline{A}^n]$ to R_n by sending X_i to $E_{i,n}$. As the induced k-algebra homomorphism is clearly surjective, we need only show that it is injective. If $F \in k[\underline{A}^n]$ maps to 0, write

$$F = f_o + f_1X_n + \dots + f_tX_n^t,$$

with $f_i \in k[\underline{A}^{n-1}]$. Setting $f_i(E_{1,n},\dots,E_{n-1,n}) = g_i$, we have

$$g_o + g_1E_{n,n} + \dots + g_tE_{n,n}^t = 0.$$

If we set $X_n = 0$ in this last equation, we obtain

$$g_o(E_{1,n-1},\dots,E_{n-1,n-1}) = 0.$$

Using induction on n, we may assume that this means that $g_o = 0$, and hence that $f_o = 0$. Therefore

$$F(E_{1,n},\dots,E_{n,n}) = E_{n,n}h(E_{1,n},\dots,E_{n,n}) = 0,$$

and so

$$h(E_{1,n},\ldots,E_{n,n}) = g_1 + g_2E_{n,n} + \ldots + g_tE_{n,n}^{t-1} = 0.$$

Repeating the argument, we see that all g_i are 0 and so all f_i are 0, i.e., $F = 0$.

The affine algebraic set whose coordinate ring is $k[V^n]^{S_n}$ is called the <u>n-th symmetric power</u> of V, and denoted by $V^{(n)}$. Our discussion above shows that the n-th symmetric power of $\underline{A}^1$ is $\underline{A}^n$.

I-7 THE FUNCTION FIELD OF AN AFFINE VARIETY

The purpose of this section is primarily terminological. Let V be an affine variety. By proposition 1.22, k[V] is a domain. We denote the fraction field of k[V] by k(V). k(V) is called the <u>field of rational functions</u> on V, or simply the <u>function field</u> of V. If $f \in k(V)$, then we can write $f = g/h$, where $g,h \in k[V]$. Then f can be regarded as a k-valued function on the open set V_h in V. One says that f is a rational function on V.

We note that if V and W are affine varieties and if a k-homomorphism of k(W) into k(V) is given, we may identify k(W) with its image in k(V). Then if $k[V] = k[f_1,\ldots,f_r]$, every element of k[W] can be expressed rationally in terms of $f_1,\ldots,f_r$. If $k[W] = k[g_1,\ldots,g_s]$, then g_i =

$F_i(f_1,\ldots,f_r)/G_i(f_1,\ldots,f_r)$, $1 \leq i \leq s$. If we set $G = G_1G_2\cdots G_s$, then the g_i belong to the ring $k[f_1,\ldots,f_r,1/G(f_1,\ldots,f_r)]$, which is the coordinate ring of $V_{G(f_1,\ldots,f_r)}$. This gives a k-morphism of this latter affine variety into W. We say that such a densely defined morphism is a <u>rational</u> <u>map</u> of V into W.

A field K is said to be finitely generated over a subfield L if there exist $f_1,\ldots,f_p \in K$ such that every element of K can be expressed as a rational function in the f_i with coefficients in L. This equivalent to K being the fraction field of the subring $L[f_1,\ldots,f_p]$. Once again we must warn the reader of a terminological ambiguity. If a field K is finitely generated as a field over L, this does <u>not</u> mean that K is a finitely generated L-algebra (unless it is an algebraic extension of L).

EXERCISE. Give a direct proof - not using Zariski's lemma - that the field k(X) of rational functions in the variable X is a finitely generated field over k but is not a finitely generated k-algebra.

We will refer to finitely generated fields over k as finitely generated extensions of k - we will only use the term 'extension' in the context of fields.

There is one other point worth noting. Suppose that R is a k-algebra which is a domain and that the fraction field of R is a finitely generated extension of k. It does not follow that R is a finitely generated k-algebra. For example, let R $= k[X, X^2Y, X^3Y^2, \ldots, X^nY^{n-1}, \ldots]$. It is easy to see that the fraction field of R is $k(X,Y)$ - the field of rational functions in X and Y - which is a finitely generated extension of k. However, R is not a finitely generated k-algebra - it is not even noetherian.

CHAPTER II

AFFINE ALGEBRAIC GROUPS

II-1 AFFINE GROUPS

The group GL_n of matrices of degree n with entries in k has the property that the entries of the product of two matrices can be expressed algebraically in terms of the entries of the factors. Also, the entries of the inverse of a matrix are algebraic functions of the entries of the matrix. This should mean that the group law on GL_n is a morphism from $GL_n \times GL_n$ to GL_n - provided, of course, that GL_n is an affine algebraic set. This is indeed the case not only for GL_n but for all the "classical" groups.

DEFINITION 2.1. An _affine group_ over k is a quadruple (G,m,i,e), where G is an affine algebraic set, $m : G \times G \to G$ is a k-morphism, $i : G \to G$ is a k-morphism, and e is a point of G, such that the following conditions hold:

i) $m(x,m(y,z)) = m(m(x,y),z)$, for all $x,y,z \in G$.

ii) $m(e,x) = x$, for all $x \in G$.

iii) $m(i(x),x) = e$, for all $x \in G$.

We will write xy for $m(x,y)$ and x^{-1} for $i(x)$.

Just as in the case of abstract groups, one proves that $xe = ex = x$ for all $x \in G$, and $xx^{-1} = x^{-1}x = e$ for all $x \in G$. All of the usual elementary properties of abstract groups apply in the case of affine groups, and we assume that the reader is sufficiently familiar with this material so that we do not need to repeat it here.

There is a "dual" definition of affine group which involves only the coordinate ring and k-algebra homomorphisms. Since this definition actually is preferable for certain purposes, we give:

DEFINITION 2.1a. A <u>Hopf</u> <u>algebra</u> over k is a quadruple (R,M,I,E), where R is a k-algebra, and M, I, and E are k-algebra homomorphisms as follows:

$$M : R \to R \otimes_k R \qquad \text{(comultiplication)}$$

$$I : R \to R \qquad \text{(coinverse)}$$

$$E : R \to k \qquad \text{(augmentation)}$$

subject to the conditions that the following diagrams commute:

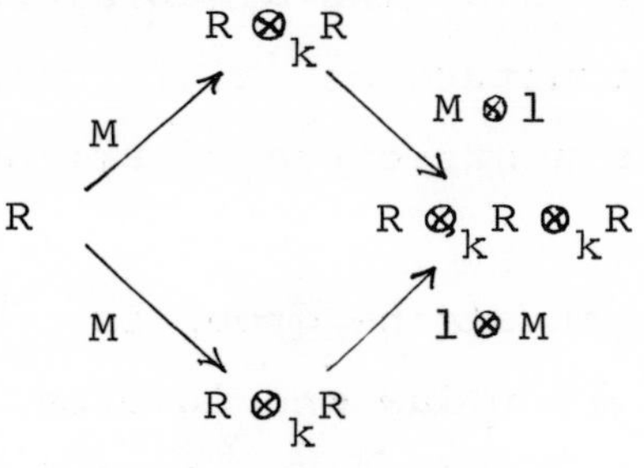

(associativity)

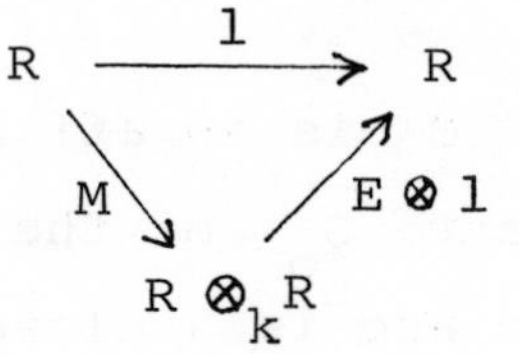

(identity)

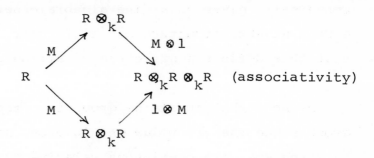

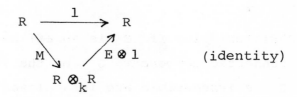

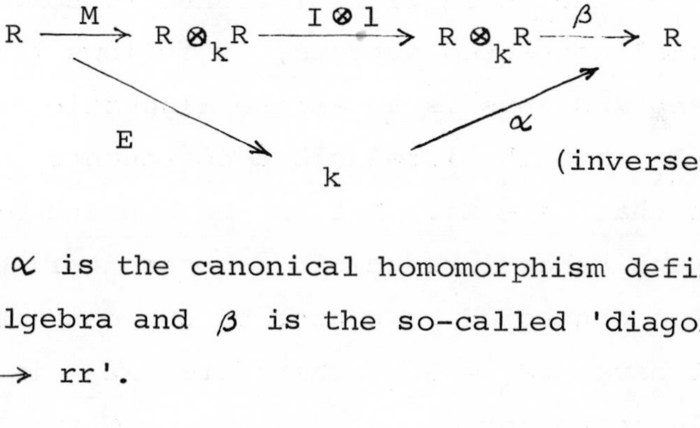

(inverse)

where α is the canonical homomorphism defining R as k-algebra and β is the so-called 'diagonal map', $r \otimes r' \mapsto rr'$.

EXERCISE. Let (G,m,i,e) be an affine group. Set $R = k[G]$, $M = \tilde{m}$, $I = \tilde{i}$, and let E be the natural mapping $R \to R/\underline{m}_o$, where $\underline{m}_o$ is the maximal ideal of R corresponding to the point e of G. Show that (R,M,I,E) is a Hopf algebra over k.

Conversely, given an affine algebraic set V, and a Hopf algebra structure on $k[V]$ over k, show that this defines a structure of affine group on V.

We note that an affine group is a topological group since the group law and inverse, being given by morphisms, are continuous relative to the Zariski topology.

PROPOSITION 2.2. If G is an affine group then the connected component G_o of the identity e of G is irreducible and is a closed normal subgroup of G.

Proof: By the definition of connected components as maximal connected subsets, it follows that G_o is closed and thus is an affine algebraic set. If $Z_1, \dots, Z_r$ are the irreducible components of G_o, suppose that $e \in Z_1$. Let z be a point of Z_i not in any other irreducible component of G_o. As zG_o is a connected component of G containing z, we must have $zG_o = G_o$. Therefore zZ_1 is an irreducible component of G_o. Since $z \in zZ_1$, we have $zZ_1 = Z_i$. Since G_o^{-1} is a connected component of G containing e, it follows that $G_o = G_o^{-1}$, whence Z_1^{-1} is an irreducible component of G_o. Taking $Z_i = Z_1^{-1}$ above, we get $Z_1^{-1}Z_1 = Z_1^{-1}$, and hence $Z_1Z_1^{-1} = Z_1$ so that Z_1 is a closed subgroup of G. But then Z_i is a coset of Z_1 in G and therefore disjoint from Z_1 unless $i = 1$. Thus $G_o = Z_1$, and therefore is an irreducible closed subgroup of G. Finally, if $x \in G$, then xG_ox^{-1} is a connected component of G containing e and therefore $xG_ox^{-1} = G_o$, so that G_o is normal in G. q.e.d.

COROLLARY 2.3. An affine group is connected if and only if it is a variety.

COROLLARY 2.4. If G is an affine group, then G/G_o is a finite group.

Proof: The cosets of G_o in G are the irreducible components of G which are finite in number by proposition 1.21.

PROPOSITION 2.5. If G is an affine group and H is a closed subgroup of G, then H is also an affine group.

Proof: The restriction of m to $H \times H$ and of i to H satisfy the requirements of definition 2.1.

REMARK. It is a highly non-trivial matter to show that if G is an affine group and N is a closed normal subgroup of G, then G/N is an affine group. We give the proof of this fact in section 6 of the present chapter.

II-2 EXAMPLES OF AFFINE GROUPS

1. The first and most important example of an affine group is GL_n, the set of $n \times n$ matrices with coefficients in k with non-zero determinant. We identify GL_n as the open set $\underline{A}_D^{n^2}$ in $\underline{A}^{n^2}$, where $D = D(X_{11},\ldots,X_{nn})$ is the determinant form. The multiplication in GL_n is the usual matrix multiplication. The comultiplication on the coordinate ring $k[GL_n] = k[X_{11},\ldots,X_{nn},1/D]$ is obviously determined by the images of the X_{ij} in $k[GL_n \times GL_n] = k[X_{11},\ldots,X_{nn},Y_{11},\ldots,Y_{nn},1/D(X)D(Y)]$. (Note that if R and R' are k-algebras, $f \in R$, $f' \in R'$, then $R[1/f] \otimes_k R'[1/f']$ is canonically isomorphic to $(R \otimes_k R')[1/f \otimes f']$.) The image of X_{ij} is just $\sum_p X_{ip}Y_{pj}$ as one would expect.

2. Let SL_n be the locus of $1 - D$ in GL_n. This is the set of matrices of determinant 1. SL_n is called the special linear group. The coordinate ring of SL_n is $k[GL_n]/(1 - D)$, and the comultiplication is given by essentially the same formula as for GL_n, viz., if x_{ij} denotes the residue of X_{ij} modulo $1 - D$, then x_{ij} is sent to $\sum_p x_{ip}y_{pj}$.

EXERCISE. Write down the formulas for the coinverse homomorphisms for GL_n and SL_n.

3. The special case $n = 1$ of GL_n is worthy of separate notice. This group is denoted by G_m and is called the multiplicative group. $k[G_m] = k[X,1/X]$, and $M(X) = XY \in k[X,Y,1/XY] = k[G_m \times G_m]$.

4. We define a group law on $\underline{A}^1$ by sending $X \in k[X] = k[\underline{A}^1]$ to $X + Y \in k[\underline{A}^2] = k[X,Y]$. The group obtained from this law is called the additive group and is denoted by G_a. Pointwise, the group law is given by $m(x,y) = x + y$.

EXERCISE. Show that the product of two affine groups is an affine group.

We recall now the definition of the tensor algebra, symmetric algebra and exterior algebra. Let R be a commutative ring with identity and let M be an R-module. Denote by T^pM the R-module $M \otimes_R M \otimes_R \cdots \otimes_R M$ (p factors). Let $T(M) = \bigoplus_{p \geq 0} T^pM$. It is readily verified that the map $T^pM \otimes T^qM \to T^{p+q}M$ given by: $(m_1 \otimes \ldots \otimes m_p) \otimes (m_1' \otimes \ldots \otimes m_q') \mapsto m_1 \otimes \ldots \otimes m_p \otimes m_1' \otimes \ldots \otimes m_q'$ makes $T(M)$ into an associative algebra, called the <u>tensor algebra</u> of M over R. $T(M)$ is a graded algebra over R and the two-sided ideals $I_s(M)$ and $I_a(M)$ in $T(M)$ generated respectively by the sets $\{m \otimes m' - m' \otimes m : m,m' \in M\}$, and $\{m \otimes m : m \in M\}$, are homogeneous.

We set $S(M) = T(M)/I_s(M)$ and $\Lambda(M) = T(M)/I_a(M)$. These algebras are graded R-algebras, called respectively the symmetric and exterior algebras of M over R. We let $S^pM = S(M)_p$ and $\overset{p}{\Lambda} M = \Lambda(M)_p$. S^pM (resp., $\overset{p}{\Lambda} M$) is called the p-th symmetric (resp., exterior) power of M. Note that S(M) is a commutative R-algebra and $\Lambda(M)$ is a skew-commutative R-algebra, i.e., if we denote by $f \wedge g$ the product of f and g in $\Lambda(M)$, then if f and g are homogeneous of degree p and q respectively, then $f \wedge g = (-1)^{pq}\, g \wedge f$. These algebras are characterized by the following universal mapping property.

> Let S be an associative (resp., associative and commutative, associative and skew-commutative) graded R-algebra. Let $\varphi: M \to S$ be a homomorphism of R-modules. Then there is a unique R-algebra homomorphism $T(\varphi): T(M) \to S$ (resp., $S(\varphi): S(M) \to S$, $\Lambda(\varphi): \Lambda(M) \to S$), whose restriction to $T^1M = S^1M = \overset{1}{\Lambda} M = M$ is φ. If $\varphi M \subset S_p$ then $T(\varphi)T^qM \subset S_{pq}$ (resp., $S(\varphi)S^qM \subset S_{pq}$, $\Lambda(\varphi) \overset{q}{\Lambda} M \subset S_{pq}$).

The proof of this is a straightforward application of the universal mapping property of the tensor product. For completeness, we recall that a graded R-algebra S is an R-algebra S together with a direct sum decomposition $S = \bigoplus_{p \in \mathbf{Z}} S_p$ where S_p

is an R-submodule of S and $S_p S_q \subset S_{p+q}$. An S-module M is a graded S-module if $M = \bigoplus_{p \in \mathbf{Z}} M_p$, where M_p is an R-submodule of M and $S_q M_p \subset M_{p+q}$. A homomorphism $\varphi : M \to N$ of graded S-modules is homogeneous of degree r if $\varphi M_p \subset N_{p+r}$. If N is a submodule of the graded S-module M, we say that N is homogeneous if N is graded and the inclusion is homogeneous of degree 0. Then M/N is a graded S-module and the projection $M \to M/N$ is homogeneous of degree 0.

EXERCISE. Let M be an n-dimensional vector space over k. Show that $\dim T^p M = n^p$, $\dim S^p M = \binom{n+p-1}{p}$ and $\dim \overset{p}{\Lambda} M = \binom{n}{p}$ for $0 \leqslant p \leqslant n$ and $\overset{p}{\Lambda} M =$ (0) otherwise.

Let U stand for any of the three 'functors' T, S, or Λ. Then we have homomorphisms $U^p : GL_n \to GL(U^p \underline{A}^n)$ given by $x \mapsto U^p(x)$. If $u \in U^p \underline{A}^n$ the set of $x \in GL_n$ such that $U^p(x)u = u$ is a subgroup of GL_n. We will see shortly that it is closed. This leads to the following examples.

5. Let $u \in S^2 \underline{A}^{n*}$ be a non-degenerate symmetric form on $\underline{A}^n$ and let $O_n(u)$ be the set of $x \in GL_n$ such that $S^2(x)^* u = u$. One then shows that $O_n(u)$ is a closed subgroup of GL_n called the <u>orthogonal</u>

group of u. We note that for any two such forms u and u', $O_n(u)$ and $O_n(u')$ are conjugate in GL_n. We can then speak of the orthogonal group O_n of degree n.

6. Let $w \in \overset{2}{\Lambda}\, \underline{A}^{2n*}$ be a non-degenerate skew form. The dimension must be even for such forms to exist. Let $Sp_n(w)$ be the set of $x \in GL_{2n}$ such that $\overset{2}{\Lambda}(x)^* w = w$. Again, all such subgroups are conjugate in GL_{2n} and we can speak of the symplectic group Sp_n.

REMARK. The groups SL_n, O_n, and Sp_n are known as the classical groups.

In order to justify our assertions in examples 5 and 6, we must look more closely at the notion of an affine group action on an affine algebraic set. This is, in fact, the proper setting for the geometric aspects of invariant theory.

II-3 ACTIONS

DEFINITION 2.6. Let G and G' be affine groups over k. A mapping $\varphi : G \to G'$ is called a k-homomorphism if it is a k-morphism such that $\varphi(xy) = \varphi(x)\varphi(y)$ for all $x, y \in G$. φ will be called a k-isomorphism if it is a k-homomorphism which is a k-isomorphism of affine algebraic sets.

DEFINITION 2.7. Let G be an affine group and let V be an affine algebraic set. By a *k-action* of G on V we mean a k-morphism $\alpha : G \times V \rightarrow V$ such that $\alpha(xy,v) = \alpha(x, \alpha(y,v))$ and $\alpha(e,v) = v$, for all $x,y \in G$, $v \in V$, e being the identity of G. We will often write $x(v)$, or simply xv for $\alpha(x,v)$.

There are two extremely important concepts connected with the notion of an action of an affine group on an affine algebraic set, viz., orbits and stabilizers.

DEFINITION 2.8. If $\alpha : G \times V \rightarrow V$ is an action of an affine group on an affine algebraic set, and v is a point of V, let $o_{\alpha}(v)$, or simply $o(v)$, be the image by α of $G \times \{v\}$ in V. $o(v)$ is called the *orbit* of v in V for the action . $o(v) = \{ xv \in V : x \in G\}$. *Note that an orbit need not be closed*.

DEFINITION 2.9. Let $\alpha : G \times V \rightarrow V$ be an action as above. Let W be a subset of V and let $S_{\alpha}(W)$, or simply $S(W)$, be the set of $x \in G$ such that $xW = W$. $S(W)$ is called the *stabilizer* of W in G.

Note that $S(W)$ is a subgroup of G.

PROPOSITION 2.10. If W is closed in V, then $S(W)$ is closed in G.

<u>Proof</u>: If $v \in W$, let $S(v,W) = \{x \in G : xv \in W\}$. Then $S(W) = \bigcap_{v \in W} S(v,W)$ so it suffices to show that each $S(v,W)$ is closed. But $S(v,W)$ is the image in G of $(G \times \{v\}) \cap \alpha^{-1}W$ under the canonical isomorphism of G with $G \times \{v\}$ and hence is closed in G.

Thus the stabilizer of a point of V is a closed subgroup of G. Indeed if $S_o(W) = \{x \in G : xv = v$ for all $v \in W\}$, then $S_o(W) = \bigcap_{v \in W} S(v)$. Therefore $S_o(W)$ is a closed subgroup of G whether or not W is closed. Next, we formulate the dual notions to homomorphisms and actions.

DEFINITION 2.6a. Let R and R' be Hopf algebras over k. A <u>cohomomorphism</u> of Hopf algebras over k is a k-algebra homomorphism $\eta : R \to R'$ such that the diagram

$$\begin{array}{ccc} R & \xrightarrow{M} & R \otimes_k R \\ \eta \downarrow & & \downarrow \eta \otimes \eta \\ R' & \xrightarrow{M'} & R' \otimes_k R' \end{array}$$

commutes, M and M' being the comultiplications

on R and R' respectively.

DEFINITION 2.7a. Let R be a Hopf algebra over k and let S be a k-algebra. By a <u>coaction</u> of R on S over k we mean a k-algebra homomorphism $A : S \to R \otimes_k S$ such that the following diagrams commute:

$$\begin{array}{ccccc} & & R \otimes_k S & & \\ & \overset{A}{\nearrow} & & \overset{M \otimes 1}{\searrow} & \\ S & & & & R \otimes_k R \otimes_k S \\ & \underset{A}{\searrow} & & \underset{1 \otimes A}{\nearrow} & \\ & & R \otimes_k S & & \end{array}$$

$$\begin{array}{ccc} S & \xrightarrow{\ \ 1\ \ } & S \\ & {\scriptstyle A}\searrow \quad \nearrow{\scriptstyle E \otimes 1} & \\ & R \otimes_k S & \end{array}$$

where M and E are the comultiplication and augmentation of R.

EXERCISE. Show that definitions 2.6a and 2.7a are indeed dual to 2.6 and 2.7, i.e., a k-homomorphism of affine groups induces a cohomomorphism of their coordinate rings, etc.

EXERCISE. Formulate the notion of stabilizer for coactions. What notion, if any, corresponds to orbits?

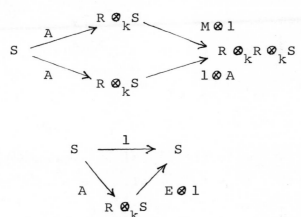

Suppose that an affine group G acts on an affine algebraic set V. Then each element of G induces a k-automorphism of V and hence a k-algebra automorphism of $k[V]$. For each $f \in k[V]$ and each $x \in G$, we define $f^x \in k[V]$ by $f^x(v) = f(xv)$. Then $x \mapsto (f \mapsto f^x)$ is a homomorphism of G into the group of k-algebra automorphisms of $k[V]$, viz., if we denote the map $f \mapsto f^x$ by U_x, then

$$U_{xx'}(f)(v) = f(xx'v) = (f^{x'})^x(v) = U_x(U_{x'}(f))(v)$$

so that $U_{xx'} = U_x \circ U_{x'}$.

DEFINITION 2.11. We denote by $k[V]^G$ the ring of G-invariant elements of $k[V]$, i.e., $k[V]^G = \{f \in k[V] : f^x = f, \text{ for all } x \in G\}$.

N.B. If $V = G$, we let G act on itself by $x(y) = yx$, i.e., by right translation.

PROPOSITION 2.12. Let the affine group G act on the affine algebraic set V. If $f \in k[V]$ then the k-vector space M spanned by all f^x, $x \in G$, is finite dimensional.

Proof: If α is the given action, then $\tilde{\alpha}(f)(x,v) = f(xv)$. Since $k[G \times V] = k[G] \otimes_k k[V]$, we may write $\tilde{\alpha}(f)(x,v) = \sum_i h_i(x)g_i(v)$, with $h_i \in k[G]$, $g_i \in k[V]$. Then $\tilde{\alpha}(f^x) = \sum_i h_i(x)g_i$, so that the g_i span M.

II-4 QUOTIENTS

If the affine group G acts on the affine algebraic set V, this action gives an equivalence relation on V, viz., $v \sim v'$ if $o(v) = o(v')$. One of the fundamental problems of invariant theory is whether - and in what sense - a quotient space for this equivalence relation exists. If we require that the quotient space be an affine algebraic set, then the general problem appears to be exceedingly difficult. I should warn the reader that the requirement that the quotient be an <u>affine</u> algebraic set is, from the most general viewpoint, unnecessarily restrictive. There are more general 'algebraic sets' which can appear as quotients of affine algebraic sets by affine groups. However, many of the most important of these can be obtained by 'gluing together' affine quotients. In any case, we shall deal only with the problem of the existence of affine quotients.

DEFINITION 2.13. Let G be an affine group. Suppose that G acts on two affine algebraic sets V and W. A k-morphism $\varphi : V \to W$ will be called a <u>G-morphism</u> (for the given actions) if $\varphi(xv) = x\varphi(v)$ for all $x \in G$, $v \in V$.

DEFINITION 2.14. Let the affine group G act on

the affine algebraic set V. We say that the action of G on V is trivial if $S_o(V) = G$. By a <u>quotient</u> of V by G (for the given action) we mean a pair (V_o, φ) where V_o is a G-trivial affine algebraic set and $\varphi: V \to V_o$ is a G-morphism such that if $\eta : V \to W$ is any G-morphism with W G-trivial, then there is a unique G-morphism $\psi : V_o \to W$ such that $\eta = \psi \circ \varphi$. (Note that the condition that ψ be a G-morphism is only that it be a k-morphism since the actions on both sides are trivial.)

For the really important applications, the above definition is too weak. The following is clearly much more geometric.

DEFINITION 2.15. Let the affine group G act on the affine algebraic set V. We say that a quotient (V_o, φ) of V by G is a <u>strict quotient</u> - or an orbit space - if the following conditions hold.

i) For each $w \in V_o$, $\varphi^{-1}(w)$ is an orbit.

ii) $U \subset V_o$ is open if and only if $\varphi^{-1}U$ is open in V.

iii) $\tilde{\varphi}$ is a k-isomorphism of $k[V_o]$ onto $k[V]^G$.

EXERCISE. Prove that a quotient of an affine algebraic set by an affine group is unique up to k-isomorphism.

EXERCISE. Show that if a pair (V_o, φ) where V_o is an affine algebraic set and $\varphi: V \to V_o$ is a k-morphism, satisfies i), ii), and iii) of definition 2.15, then (V_o, φ) is already a quotient in the sense of definition 2.14.

For an example of how things can easily go bad, consider GL_2 acting on $\underline{A}^2$ in the standard way. It is clear that a strict quotient cannot exist here because i) of definition 2.15 implies that orbits must be closed. In this case, there is one open orbit, $\underline{A}^2 - \{(0,0)\}$, and one closed orbit, $\{(0,0)\}$. The difficulties in this case arise from the presence of a fixed point. This phenomenon always complicates matters. However, even if there are no fixed points, strict quotients - and even quotients - may fail to exist. For examples and counterexamples to this subtle problem, see: D. Mumford, <u>Geometric Invariant Theory</u>.

EXERCISE. For the action of S_n on $\underline{A}^n$ discussed in I-6, show that the n-th symmetric power of $\underline{A}^1$ $(= \underline{A}^n)$ is a strict quotient of $\underline{A}^n$ by S_n.

EXERCISE. Formulate the notion of quotient (perhaps 'coquotient' would be better) for coactions. Why is it harder to formulate the notion of strict quotient for coactions?

II-5 REPRESENTATIONS OF AFFINE GROUPS

LEMMA 2.16. Let $\varphi : V \to V'$ be a k-morphism of affine varieties. If U is a non-empty open subset of V, then φU contains a non-empty open subset of $\overline{\varphi U}$.

Proof: Since V is irreducible, U is dense in V and irreducible. Thus φU is irreducible and hence $\overline{\varphi U}$ is irreducible. Thus we may assume that $V' = \overline{\varphi U}$.

Let $R = k[V]$ and $R' = k[V']$. If $\tilde{\varphi}(f) = 0$, then $f \mid \varphi U = 0$, and as φU is dense in V', it follows that $f = 0$. Thus $\tilde{\varphi}$ is injective. We will identify R' as a subring of R. Then we may write $R = R'[f_1,\ldots,f_n]$ for suitable $f_i \in R$, since R is finitely generated over k and *a fortiori* finitely generated over R'. If V_i is an affine model of $R'[f_1,\ldots,f_i]$ and $\varphi_i: V_i \to V_{i-1}$ is the k-morphism induced by the inclusion $R'[f_1,\ldots,f_{i-1}] \subset R'[f_1,\ldots,f_i]$, it clearly suffices to prove the lemma for each φ_i. Thus we may assume that $R = R'[f]$.

Case 1. f is transcendental over R', i.e., over k(V'). Then R is isomorphic to the polynomial ring R'[X]. If $\underline{m}'$ is a maximal ideal of R', then $\underline{m}'R \cap R' = \underline{m}'$ so that φ is surjective. As U is open in V, there is a $g \in R$ such that $V_g \subset U$. If $g = a_o + a_1 f + \ldots + a_n f^n$, $a_i \in R'$, then

$$\varphi V_g = \bigcup_{i=0}^{n} V'_{a_i} \subset \varphi U ,$$

and each V'_{a_i} is open in V'. Since $U \neq \emptyset$, we may choose $g \neq 0$ and then at least one $a_i \neq 0$. But then $V'_{a_i} \neq \emptyset$.

Case 2. f is algebraic over R', i.e., over k(V'). Then g is also algebraic. If

$$b_n g^n + b_{n-1} g^{n-1} + \ldots + b_o = 0$$

is a minimal equation for g over k(V') then, clearing denominators, we may assume that $b_i \in R'$, $b_n \neq 0$. Replacing g by $h = b_n g$, we get

$$h^n + b_{n-1} h^{n-1} + b_n b_{n-2} h^{n-2} + \ldots + b_n^{n-1} b_o = 0.$$

Also, V_h is a non-empty open subset of V_g. If $b = b_n^{n-1} b_o$ then $b(v) \neq 0$ implies $h(v)^n \neq 0$, so $h(v) \neq 0$, for $v \in V$. Thus $\varphi^{-1} V'_b \subset V_h \subset U$. But $\varphi\varphi^{-1} V'_b = V'_b \subset \varphi U$, and V'_b is open. On the other hand, $b = 0$ implies $b_o = 0$, but since a minimal equation of g is irreducible, $b_o \neq 0$. Hence $V'_b \neq \emptyset$. q.e.d.

LEMMA 2.17. Let G be a connected affine group. If U is a non-empty open subset of G, then $G = UU$.

Proof: If $x \in G$, then $U \cap xU^{-1} \neq \emptyset$ so we can find $u_i \in U$, $i = 1,2$, with $u_1 = xu_2^{-1}$, i.e., $x = u_1 u_2$.

COROLLARY 2.18. Let G be an affine group and let H be a connected subgroup of G. If H contains a non-empty open subset of $\overline{H}$ then H is closed.

Proof: By lemma 2.17, if $U \subset H$ is non-empty and open in $\overline{H}$ then $UU = \overline{H}$. But $U \subset H$ implies $H = \overline{H}$.

COROLLARY 2.19. If $\varphi : G \to G'$ is a k-homomorphism of affine groups, then φG is a closed subgroup of G'.

Proof: We may clearly assume that G is connected. Then φG is a connected subgroup of G', and, by lemma 2.16, it contains a non-empty open subset of $\overline{\varphi G}$. By 2.18, φG is closed.

The next theorem, due to Chevalley, asserts that a closed subgroup H of an affine group G is determined by its semi-invariants, i.e., those $f \in k[G]$ such that the subspace spanned by f^x, $x \in H$, is one-dimensional.

THEOREM 2.20. Let G be an affine group and let H be a closed subgroup of G. Then there exist elements $f_1,\ldots,f_r,\chi \in k[G]$ such that $H = \{x \in G : f_i^x = \chi(x)f_i,\ 1 \leqslant i \leqslant r\}$.

<u>Proof</u>: Let $g_1,\ldots,g_t$ generate $\underline{I}_G(H)$. Let M be the subspace of $k[G]$ spanned by all g_i^x, $x \in G$. By 2.12, M is finite dimensional. M is also stable under the action of G on $k[G]$, i.e., $f \in M$ implies $f^x \in M$. Since $I = \underline{I}_G(H)$ is H-stable, $N = M \cap I$ is H-stable. Conversely, $N^x = N$ implies $I^x = I$, since $I = Nk[G]$. Then $f^x(e) = f(x) = 0$ for all $f \in I$ so $x \in H$. If $\dim N = d$, then $\overset{d}{\Lambda} N$ is a one-dimensional subspace of $\overset{d}{\Lambda} M$. If we use the same notation for the action of G on $\overset{d}{\Lambda} M$, then given $0 \neq u \in \overset{d}{\Lambda} N$, $x \in H$ if and only if $u^x \in \overset{d}{\Lambda} N$.

Let $e_o = u, e_1,\ldots, e_r$ be a basis of $\overset{d}{\Lambda} M$, and let $(f_{ij}(x))$ be the matrix of the action of $x \in G$ with respect to this basis, $f_{ij} \in k[G]$. Then $H = \{x \in G : f_{oi}(x) = 0,\ 1 \leqslant i \leqslant r\}$. Now $(f_{ij}(yx)) = (f_{ij}(x))(f_{ij}(y))$ so

$$f_{ij}(yx) = \sum_p f_{ip}(x)f_{pj}(y) .$$

Then $f_{oj}(yx) = f_{oo}(x)f_{oj}(y)$, i.e., $f_{oj}^x = f_{oo}(x)f_{oj}$, for $x \in H$, $y \in G$. We set $f_j = f_{oj}$, $1 \leqslant j \leqslant r$, and $\chi = f_{oo}$. Now if $x \in G$ and $f_j^x = \chi(x)f_j$, $1 \leqslant j \leqslant r$, it follows that $f_j(yx) = \chi(x)f_j(y)$ for all $y \in G$ so $f_j(x) = \chi(x)f_j(e) = 0$ so $x \in H$.

COROLLARY 2.21. Let G be an affine group and let N be a closed normal subgroup of G. Then there is an integer n and a k-homomorphism $\rho : G \to GL_n$ with kernel N.

Proof: Choose $f_1, \ldots, f_r, \chi \in k[G]$ such that $N = \{x \in G : f_i^x = \chi(x)f_i,\ 1 \leqslant i \leqslant r\}$. Let M be the subspace of $k[G]$ spanned by all f_i^x, $x \in G$, $1 \leqslant i \leqslant r$. Then $f^x = \chi(x)f$ for all $f \in M$. To see this last assertion, suppose $x \in N$, $y \in G$. Then $(f_i^y)^x = f_i^{xy} = f_i^{yx'} = (f_i^{x'})^y$ for some $x' \in N$, as N is normal in G. Then $(f_i^{x'})^y = (\chi(x')f_i)^y = \chi(x')f_i^y$. But for any $x \in N$, $y \in G$, $\chi(xy) = \chi(yy^{-1}xy) = \chi(y)\chi(y^{-1}xy) = \chi(y)\chi(x)$ so that $\chi(y^{-1}xy) = \chi(x)$. Therefore $\chi(x')f_i^y = \chi(x)f_i^y$ and thus $(f_i^y)^x = \chi(x)f_i^y$. Since the f_i^y span M, the assertion is proved.

Now $U_x : M \to M$ is a scalar mapping if and only if the mapping ${}^tU_x^{-1} \otimes U_x$ is the identity on $M^* \otimes M$. Thus if we set $\rho(x) = {}^tU_x^{-1} \otimes U_x$, then $\rho : G \to GL(M^* \otimes M)$ is a k-homomorphism with kernel N. If $p = \dim M$, then $GL(M^* \otimes M)$ is k-isomorphic to GL_n, $n = p^2$.

COROLLARY 2.22. If G is an affine group then G is k-isomorphic to a closed subgroup of GL_n for some n.

Proof: Apply corollary 2.21 with $N = (e)$ to obtain a bijective k-homomorphism $\rho: G \to \rho G \subset GL_n$ for a suitable n. By 2.19, ρG is a closed subgroup of GL_n. It remains to prove that ρ^{-1} is a k-morphism. To do this it will suffice to show that $\tilde{\rho} : k[GL_n] \to k[G]$ is surjective. Let $k[G] = k[f_1,\ldots,f_n]$ and let M be the subspace of $k[G]$ spanned by the translates f_i^x of the f_i, $x \in G$. Let $g_1,\ldots,g_m$ be a basis of M. Note that if x acts trivially on M, then $x = e$. Now it suffices to find $F_i \in k[GL_n]$ such that $F_i \circ \rho = g_i$, $1 \leqslant i \leqslant m$. We have

$$g_i^x = \sum_j \rho_{ji}(x) g_j \quad ,$$

$$g_i^{xy} = \sum_j \rho_{ji}(y) g_j(x) \quad .$$

Therefore

$$g_i^x = \sum_j \rho_{ji} g_j(e).$$

Let $F_i(X_{11},\ldots,X_{nn}) = \sum_j X_{ji} g_j(e)$. Then $F_i(\rho(x)) = \sum_j \rho_{ji}(x) g_j(e) = g_i^x(e) = g_i(x)$. q.e.d.

This shows that any affine group is a closed subgroup of GL_n for some n. In other words, every affine group is a linear group. There are more general algebraic groups than the linear ones, but they are not affine. However, the only truly different types of algebraic group are all closed subsets of suitable projective spaces - the so-called abelian varieties. One then shows that if G is any algebraic group, then there is a maximal linear subgroup G_o in G (which is necessarily normal in G) and G/G_o is an abelian variety.

DEFINITION 2.23. Let M be a finite dimensional vector space over k. Then M can be regarded as a variety over k, with coordinate ring $S(M^*)$. Also $GL(M)$ has a natural structure of affine group. A <u>representation</u> of an affine group G in M is a homomorphism $\rho: G \to GL(M)$. If ρ is a k-homomorphism we say that ρ is a <u>rational representation</u> and that M is a <u>rational G-module</u>. If M is not finite dimensional and we are given a representation $\rho: G \to GL(M)$, we say that M is a rational G-module if it is the union of finite dimensional rational G-modules, i.e., every $m \in M$ is contained in a finite dimensional G-stable subspace N and the restriction of the action of G to N is a rational representation of G in N.

If G is an affine group and M is a finite dimensional rational G-module, then, regarding M

as a variety, we see that this is just a special kind of action of G on M.

As an example of a rational G-module we may take $M = k[G]$ with the representation $\rho(x)f = f^x$. This G-module has the following striking property. If N is any finite dimensional rational G-module, then N is G-isomorphic to a G-submodule of $k[G]^n$ for some n. To see this, let χ be an element of N^* and define $\hat{\chi} : N \to k[G]$ by $\hat{\chi}(n)(x) = \chi(xn)$. Then $\hat{\chi}(xn)(y) = \chi(yxn) = \hat{\chi}(n)(yx) = \hat{\chi}(n)^x(y)$, for $x,y \in G$, $n \in N$. Thus $n \mapsto \hat{\chi}(n)$ is a G-homomorphism of N into $k[G]$. If $\chi_1,\ldots,\chi_n$ is a basis of N^* then we can define $(\chi_1,\ldots,\chi_n)^\wedge : N \to k[G]^n$ by $(\chi_1,\ldots,\chi_n)^\wedge(m) = (\chi_1(m),\ldots,\chi_n(m))$ for $m \in N$. Clearly $(\chi_1,\ldots,\chi_n)^\wedge$ is an injective G-homomorphism.

Furthermore, if N has no G-submodules but N and (0), then if $\chi \in N^*$ is not zero, $n \mapsto \hat{\chi}(n)$ is necessarily injective. Thus $k[G]$ itself contains every irreducible rational representation of G.

One says that a representation $\rho : G \to GL(M)$ of a group G is faithful if its kernel is trivial. Then corollary 2.22 asserts that an affine group has a faithful rational representation in a finite dimensional vector space, and corollary 2.21 says that there are enough finite dimensional rational representations to distinguish closed normal subgroups.

II-6 QUOTIENTS OF AFFINE GROUPS BY CLOSED NORMAL SUBGROUPS

If G is an abstract group and N is a normal subgroup then it is an easy matter to construct the quotient group G/N. Now corollary 2.21 solves the following problem: given an affine group G and a closed normal subgroup N, find an affine group H and a surjective k-homomorphism of G to H with kernel N. However, we did not do this by constructing a quotient. The problem which we take up now is to construct a strict quotient of G by the action of N by right translation. There is a subtle difference between these two problems, and our solution of the first is only the starting point for our solution of the second. Before beginning we need two algebro-geometric lemmas.

LEMMA 2.24. Let $\varphi : V \to W$ be a bijective k-morphism of affine varieties. Then $k(V)$ is a purely inseparable extension of $k(W)$, i.e., if k has characteristic $p > 0$, then for each $f \in k(V)$, $f^{p^n} \in k(W)$ for some n, and if k has characteristic 0, then $k(V) = k(W)$.

<u>Proof</u>: First we show that $k(V)$ is algebraic over $k(W)$. If not, let $t \in k(V)$ be transcendental over

$k(W)$. If $t = f/g$, $f, g \in k[V]$ and f and g are algebraic over $k(W)$, then so is t. Thus we may assume that $t \in k[V]$. The inclusions $k[W] \subset k[W][t] \subset k[V]$ induce k-morphisms

$$V \xrightarrow{\psi} W \times \underline{A}^1 \xrightarrow{\eta} W$$

whose composite is φ. If $\overline{\psi V} = W \times \underline{A}^1$, then ψV contains a non-empty open set U in $W \times \underline{A}^1$ and then, for some $w \in W$, $U \cap (\{w\} \times \underline{A}^1)$ is non-empty and open in $\{w\} \times \underline{A}^1$. This means that $U \cap (\{w\} \times \underline{A}^1)$ is infinite, contradicting the injectivity of φ. Therefore $\overline{\psi V}$ is a proper closed subset of $W \times \underline{A}^1$ and therefore there is an $f \in k[W][t]$ such that $f \neq 0$ and $f | \psi V = 0$. Then $\tilde{\psi} f = 0$, which is a contradiction. Thus $k(V)$ is a finite algebraic extension of $k(W)$.

Let K be the separable closure of $k(W)$ in $k(V)$ and let f be a primitive element for K over $k(W)$, i.e., $K = k(W)(f)$. We will show that $K = k(W)$. First note that f can be chosen in $k[V]$. To see this, let $f = g/h$ with $g, h \in k[V]$. Since K is separable over $k(W)$, $k(W)(f) = k(W)(f^p)$, where p is the characteristic, $p > 0$. Then $k(W)(f) = k(W)(f^{p^n})$ for any $n > 0$. Since $k(V)$ is purely inseparable over K, we can find an n such that $g^{p^n}, h^{p^n} \in K$. Thus we may assume that $g, h \in K \cap k[V]$. Denoting this last ring by R, we see that K is the fraction field of R.

Now let

$$S = R \otimes_{k[W]} k(W) .$$

Then S is a field containing R, so $S = K$. Thus we can write $f = \sum a_i g_i$, $a_i \in R$, $g_i \in k(W)$. Then there is an $a \in k[W]$ with $af \in R$ and af is still primitive for K over $k(W)$. This shows that f can be chosen in $k[V]$ when the characteristic is $p > 0$. If the characteristic is 0 then $K = k(V)$. We can then take $R = k[V]$ and argue as above.

Now the inclusions $k[W] \subset k[W][f] \subset k[V]$ induce k-morphisms

$$V \xrightarrow{\psi} W' \xrightarrow{\eta} W ,$$

where W' is an affine model of $k[W][f]$. As before ψV must be dense in W'. If U' is an open set in W' contained in ψV, and U is a non-empty open set in W contained in $\eta U'$, then we may choose $g \in k[W]$, $g \neq 0$ so that $W_g \subset U$. Then $\eta^{-1} W_g \subset U'$ and $\varphi^{-1} W_g = V_g$. Therefore we may assume that ψ and η are surjective and hence that η is bijective.

This means that we are reduced to proving that if $\eta : W' \to W$ is a bijective k-morphism of affine varieties and $k(W')$ is separable over $k(W)$ then $k(W') = k(W)$. As before, we assume that $k[W'] = k[W][f]$ where f is primitive for $k(W')$ over $k(W)$. If $F(f) = 0$ is a minimal equation for f over $k(W)$ then F has no multiple roots in the algebraic closure of $k(W)$. Therefore the resultant $r(F,F') \neq 0$. Since $r \in k(W)$, r is a rational function on W and there is a non-empty open set U in W such that $r(w) \neq 0$ for all $w \in U$, i.e., $r = s/t$, $s,t \in k[W]$ and $s(w) \neq 0 \neq t(w)$. If $F = \sum a_i X^i$ $a_i \in k(W)$, we may assume that $a_i \in k[W]$ and hence that $F(w,X) = \sum a_i(w)X^i$ has distinct roots in k for all $w \in U$. But the roots of $F(w,X)$ may be identified with the points of $W' \subset W \times \underline{A}^1$ which lie over w. Since these are distinct, there can only be one such point. If we take $w \in U \cap (\bigcup_i W_{a_i})$, we see that F has degree 1, i.e., $k(W) = k(W')$, and the lemma is proved.

The next lemma shows that - in contrast to the problem of finite generation of rings of invariants - the problem of finite generation of fields of invariants is trivial.

LEMMA 2.25. Let K be a field, and let E be a finitely generated extension field of K. If L is a subfield of E containing K, then L is also a finitely generated extension of K.

Proof: Fix a transcendence basis $u_1,\ldots,u_t$ for L over K and extend this to a transcendence basis $u_1,\ldots,u_t,v_1,\ldots,v_s$ for E over K. Then E is algebraic over $K(u,v)$ and hence of finite degree over $K(u,v)$. We show that L is of finite degree over $K(u)$. If not, then given $n > 0$ we can find $f_1, \ldots, f_n \in L$ which are linearly independent over $K(u)$. Now if $\sum a_i f_i = 0$, $a_i \in K(u,v)$, and some $a_i \neq 0$, then $v_1, \ldots, v_s$ are algebraically dependent over L and hence over a finite galois extension L_o of $K(u)$. If $F(v_1, \ldots, v_s) = 0$, with $F \in L_o[X_1, \ldots, X_s]$, let $G(X) = N_{L_o/K(u)}(F(X))$ be the norm polynomial of F. Then $G(v_1, \ldots, v_s) = 0$, and G has coefficients in a purely inseparable extension L_1 of $K(u)$. Then if $G^{(p^n)}$ denotes the polynomial resulting from raising the coefficients of G to the p^n-th power, then $G^{(p^n)}$ has coefficients in $K(u)$ for a suitable n, and $G^{(p^n)}(v_1, \ldots, v_s) = 0$, which is a contradiction. Thus $f_1, \ldots, f_n$ are linearly independent over $K(u,v)$ and so E has infinite degree over $K(u,v)$, contradicting our initial hypotheses.

THEOREM 2.26. Let G be an affine group and let N be a closed normal subgroup of G. Then a strict quotient of G by N exists. This quotient is an affine group, and the quotient morphism is a k-homomorphism with kernel N.

Proof: We prove the theorem first in the case where G is connected. The initial - and hardest - step will be to show that the ring $k[G]^N$ is a finitely generated k-algebra.

By corollary 2.21, we can find a k-homomorphism $\rho: G \to GL_n$ with kernel N. Let R be the coordinate ring of the closed subgroup ρG of GL_n and let $R_o = \tilde{\rho} R$. Let K be the fraction field of R and let $K_o = \tilde{\rho} K$ be the fraction field of R_o. We proceed in several steps.

1. $k[G]^N = k(G)^N \cap k[G]$. This is obvious.

2. $R_o = K_o \cap k[G]$. Clearly $R_o \subset K_o \cap k[G]$. Conversely, suppose $F = f/g$ with $f, g \in R_o$ and that g is not in any maximal ideal of k[G]. If $g = \tilde{\rho}(g')$, $f = \tilde{\rho}(f')$ with $f', g' \subset R$, then since $\rho : G \to \rho G$ is surjective, g' must be a unit of R so that $f'/g' \in R$, whence $F \in R_o$.

3. $R_o = K_o \cap k[G]^N$. This follows from 1 and 2.

4. By lemma 2.25, $k(G)^N$ is a finitely generated extension of k so we may write $k(G)^N = k(g_1, \ldots, g_n)$, $g_i \in k(G)^N$. Let $R_1 = k[g_1, \ldots, g_n]$ and let V_1 be the affine model of R_1 defined by the g_i's.

5. Write $R_o = k[f_1, \ldots, f_m]$. Then if $f_i = F_i(g_1, \ldots, g_n)/G_i(g_1, \ldots, g_n)$, let $G_o = G_1 G_2 \cdots G_m$ and let $V' = (V_1)_{G_o(g_1, \ldots, g_n)}$. Then V' is an affine variety and $R_o \subset k[V'] = k[g_1, \ldots, g_n, 1/g]$, where $g = G_o(g_1, \ldots, g_n)$. This yields a k-morphism $\vartheta: V' \to \rho G$ via the isomorphism of R with R_o induced by $\tilde{\rho}$. I claim that ϑ is injective.

To prove this assertion, let $U = G_g$. Then the

inclusion $k[V'] \subset k[G][1/g]$ induces a k-morphism $\eta : U \to V'$ such that $\rho | U = \vartheta \circ \eta$. Now if x, x' are points of U and $x' \in xN$ then $\rho(x) = \rho(x')$. If $\eta(x) \neq \eta(x')$ then there is an $f \in k[V']$ such that $f(x) \neq f(x')$ - f being regarded as a k-valued function on U. But $f \in k(G)^N$ so that f must be constant on cosets of N.

U is a non-empty open subset of G so ρU contains a non-empty open subset of ρG. We may assume that $U_1 = (\rho G)_h \subset \rho G$ for some $h \in R$, $h \neq 0$. Let $h' = \tilde{\rho}(h)$. Then $U_o = U_{h'}$ and $U' = V'_h$ are affine varieties and $U_o = \eta^{-1} U'$. Thus, replacing U, V', and ρG by affine open subvarieties, we may assume that η is surjective. Then for $y, y' \in V'$, there exist $x, x' \in U$ with $y = \eta(x)$, $y' = \eta(x')$ so that $\vartheta(y) = \vartheta(y')$ implies $\rho(x) = \rho(x')$ and hence $x' \in xN$. By the same argument as before, there cannot be a function in $k[V']$ separating y and y' so that $y = y'$. This proves our assertion and shows that we may assume that V' is mapped bijectively onto an open set W in ρG, that W is an affine variety, and that $k[W] \subset k[V']$.

6. By lemma 2.24, $k(V')$ is a purely inseparable extension of $k(W) = K_o$. This means that if the characteristic is 0 then we are finished, as $k(G)^N = k(V') = K_o$, so by 3, $k[G]^N = R_o$. Thus we will assume now that the characteristic is $p > 0$. Then

we know that $f \in k[G]^N$ implies $f^{p^n} \in R_o$ for some n.

7. Let $L = k(G)^N$. Since L is a finite extension of K_o there is an n such that $L^{p^n} \subset K_o$. Let S be the set of all $f \in K_o^{p^{-n}}$ such that $f^{p^n} \in R_o$. Then S is a subring of $K_o^{p^{-n}}$ and $f \mapsto f^{p^n}$ gives an isomorphism of S onto R_o. This is not a k-isomorphism, but since k is algebraically closed it is mapped onto itself by this isomorphism. Thus $S = k[f_1^{p^{-n}}, \ldots, f_m^{p^{-n}}]$. S is then generated, as R_o-module, by the monomials

$$f_1^{i_1 p^{-n}} f_2^{i_2 p^{-n}} \cdots f_m^{i_m p^{-n}} \quad , \quad i_j \leqslant p^n ,$$

and there are p^{nm} of these. Hence S is a finitely generated R_o-module. On the other hand, $k[G]^N \subset S$ and since R_o is noetherian, it follows from proposition 1.17 that $k[G]^N$ is a finitely generated R_o-module, and <u>a fortiori</u> a finitely generated R_o-algebra. As R_o is finitely generated over k, it follows that $k[G]^N$ is finitely generated over k. This completes the first step.

Now let V be an affine model of $k[G]^N$. V is unique up to k-isomorphism. The inclusion $R_o \subset k[G]^N$ induces a k-morphism $\psi : V \to \rho G$. To see that ψ is surjective, we must invoke the results of chapter III, section 1. Let $\underline{m}$ be a maximal ideal of R_o and let T be the multiplicative set

$R_o - \underline{m}$. Then $T^{-1}(k[G]^N)$ is a finitely generated $T^{-1}R_o$-module, so by Nakayama's lemma (3.9),

$$\underline{m}(T^{-1}(k[G]^N)) \neq T^{-1}(k[G]^N) \quad ,$$

whence $\underline{m}(k[G]^N) \neq k[G]^N$ and we can find a maximal ideal $\underline{n}$ in $k[G]^N$ such that $\underline{n} \cap R_o = \underline{m}$. To see that ψ is injective, let $\underline{n}$, $\underline{n}'$ be maximal ideals of $k[G]^N$ such that $\underline{n} \cap R_o = \underline{n}' \cap R_o$. Then for any $f \in \underline{n}$, $f^{p^r} \in \underline{n}'$ for some r. Thus $\underline{n} = \underline{n}'$.

Since ψ is bijective, the morphism $\varphi : G \to V$ induced by $k[G]^N \subset k[G]$ is surjective. The conditions i) and iii) of definition 2.15 are immediate from the construction of V - the inverse image of a point of V is a coset of N. It remains only to show that ii) holds. For this it suffices to show that if U is an open neighborhood of e in G, then U contains an open neighborhood of $e' = \rho(e)$. It is well known that there exists an open neighborhood V of e in G such that $VV^{-1} \subset U$. Let V' be a non-empty open subset of ρV. If $x' \in V'$, choose $x \in V$ with $x' = \rho(x)$. Then $Vx^{-1} \subset U$ so $V'x'^{-1} \subset \rho U$. But $V'x'^{-1}$ is open and contains e'. (This proves, in fact, that a surjective k-homomorphism of affine groups is an open mapping.) On the other hand, as ψ is bijective and purely inseparable, it is a homeomorphism, viz., $V_f = (\rho G)_{f^{p^n}}$ as soon as $f^{p^n} \in R_o$.

It remains to prove that V is an affine group and is a homomorphism. If $x \in N$, $y \in G$, then there is an $x' \in N$ such that $yx = x'y$. Therefore left and right N-invariance are equivalent. If $y, y' \in G$, then

$$f(yy') = (\tilde{m}f)(y,y') = \sum g_i(y)h_i(y') ,$$

$g_i, h_i \in k[G]$. Thus if $f \in k[G]^N$, $x \in N$, $y, y' \in G$, then

$$f(yxy') = f(yy'x') = \sum g_i(y)h_i(y') ,$$

i.e., $f^y = f^{yx} = \sum g_i(yx)h_i = \sum g_i(y)h_i$. Since we may assume that the h_i are linearly independent over k, and since this holds for all y, it follows that $g_i^x = g_i$. Using the equivalence of left and right invariance, we see that $h_i^x = h_i$. Thus the diagram

$$\begin{array}{ccc} k[G] & \xrightarrow{\tilde{m}} & k[G] \otimes_k k[G] \\ \uparrow & & \uparrow \\ k[G]^N & \xrightarrow{\tilde{m}|k[G]^N} & k[G]^N \otimes_k k[G]^N \end{array}$$

commutes, the vertical maps being the inclusions. Moreover, for $f \in k[G]$, $y \in G$, $(\tilde{i}f)(y) = f(y^{-1})$, so if $x \in N$ and $f \in k[G]^N$, then $(\tilde{i}f)^x(y) = f(x^{-1}y^{-1}) = f(y^{-1}x'^{-1}) = f^{x'^{-1}}(y^{-1}) = f(y^{-1}) = (\tilde{i}f)(y)$. Therefore i maps $k[G]^N$ to itself. Finally, the augmentation E of $k[G]$ induces an augmentation of $k[G]^N$ since the composite mapping $k[G]^N \to k[G] \xrightarrow{E} k$ is a k-algebra homomorphism.

Since the Hopf operations on $k[G]^N$ arise by restriction , all the required commutativities hold. This shows that V is an affine group and φ is a k-homomorphism.

In the case where G is not connected, we set $N' = N \cap G_o$, where G_o is the connected component of e in G. Then N' is a closed normal subgroup of G_o and hence a strict quotient G_o/N' exists. If G_i is a connected component of G, then G_i is a coset of G_o - say $G_i = xG_o$. Then multiplication by x is an N'-isomorphism of G_o onto G_i. Therefore, a strict quotient of G_i by N' exists, which we denote by V_i. If we take G/N' to be the disjoint union of the V_i, it is clear how to make G/N' into an affine group and how to define a surjective k-homomorphism of G onto G/N', making G/N' a strict quotient of G by N'.

The image of N in G/N' is a finite group. Thus we are reduced to showing that a strict quotient of an affine group G by a finite normal subgroup N such that $N \cap G_o = (e)$, exists. This, however, is a trivial exercise which we leave to the reader.

REMARK. Actually we shall show in chapter V that a strict quotient of any affine algebraic set by a finite group always exists. It is also possible to prove that if G is an affine group and H is a closed (but not necessarily normal) subgroup of G, then a strict quotient of G by H exists. However, G/H may not be an affine algebraic set. For example, GL_2/H, where H is the subgroup of matrices $\begin{pmatrix} a & 0 \\ c & b \end{pmatrix}$ is easily seen to be just the projective line.

As we have developed no technique for dealing with this type of quotient, we leave the problem aside. Nevertheless, we have proved most of the technical lemmas required for such a construction, and the reader who is familiar with abstract varieties will have no difficulty in carrying it out.

We add some remarks on representations of affine groups. If G is an affine group and M is a finite dimensional rational G-module, we make M* into a rational G-module by letting $x\chi = (\rho(x)^{-1})^*\chi$, $x \in G$, $\chi \in M^*$, ρ being the given k-homomorphism of G into GL(M). This is called the contragredient representation of ρ. In this way the modules $T^pM \otimes T^qM^*$ become rational G-modules via the functorial properties of the tensor product. More specifically, we have:

EXERCISE. If M and N are finite dimensional rational G-modules, and $\rho : G \to GL(M)$ and $\sigma : G \to GL(N)$ are the given k-homomorphisms, show that $x \mapsto \rho(x) \otimes \sigma(x)$ makes $M \otimes N$ into a rational G-module.

If M and N are finite dimensional rational G-modules, then the module $\mathrm{Hom}_k(M,N)$ of k-linear mappings of M into N is canonically isomorphic to $M^* \otimes N$ so it too becomes a rational G-module.

EXERCISE. If M is a finite dimensional rational G-module, show that the modules $S^p M$ and $\overset{p}{\Lambda} M$ are rational G-modules in a natural way.

These representations play a central role in the classical invariant theory of forms. For a brief but excellent discussion of the representations of GL_n, see: R.Hartshorne, Ample Vector Bundles, (Publ. Math. IHES, no. 29).

As an example of a representation of an affine group which is not rational, take k to be the complex number field and to be the exponential map from G_a to $G_m = GL_1$. For an example of a representation of G_a in a complex vector space M such that M is not the union of finite dimensional G_a-submodules, take $M = L^1(\mathbf{C})$, $\mathbf{C}$ = complex line, and note that if we let $(xf)(z) = f(z + x)$, then the function e^{-z^2} does not lie in a finite dimensional G_a-submodule.

CHAPTER III

AFFINE GROUPS AND LIE ALGEBRAS

III-1 SOME LOCAL ALGEBRA

We will only touch briefly on a very extensive topic. We have seen in chapter I that the geometry on an affine algebraic set V is completely determined by the algebra of its coordinate ring $k[V]$. In this section we introduce the notion of localization and indicate how one may use it to study the geometry on V at one of its points. The convention about k being an algebraically closed field is still in force, and unless otherwise specified, all rings are commutative rings with identity.

DEFINITION 3.1. If R is a ring, a *multiplicative set* in R is a non-empty subset T of R such that $f,g \in T$ implies $fg \in T$. (Some authors stipulate that T not contain 0 or that T contain no zero-divisors, but we make no such restriction.)

DEFINITION 3.2. If T is a multiplicative set in the ring R, let (X_t) be a set of variables indexed by the elements of T. We denote by $R[(X_t)]$ the ring of polynomials in the (possibly infinite) set of variables X_t. Elements of $R[(X_t)]$ are polynomials of the form

$$\sum a_{t_1 \ldots t_r}^{i_1 \ldots i_r} X_{t_1}^{i_1} \ldots X_{t_r}^{i_r}, \quad X_{t_j} \in (X_t), \quad a_{t_1 \ldots t_r}^{i_1 \ldots i_r} \in R$$

where the sum is a finite sum. In $R[(X_t)]$ we let I_T be the ideal generated by all elements of the form $tX_t - 1$, and we set $T^{-1}R = R[(X_t)]/I_T$. If $a \in R$, we let $\varphi_T(a)$ be the image of $a \in R \subset R[(X_t)]$ by the canonical homomorphism $R[(X_t)] \to R[(X_t)]/I_T$. $T^{-1}R$ is called the <u>ring of T-fractions</u> of R or the <u>localization</u> of R at T.

PROPOSITION 3.3. (Universal mapping property of localizations) Let $\eta : R \to S$ be a homomorphism of rings such that for all $t \in T$, $\eta(t)$ is a unit of S. Then there is a unique homomorphism ζ: $T^{-1}R \to S$ such that $\eta = \zeta \circ \varphi_T$.

<u>Proof</u>: We remark that if we allow (0) as a ring, then we must regard 0 as a unit of (0). Now to define ζ we map X_t to $1/\eta(t)$, which induces a homomorphism of $R[(X_t)]$ into S whose kernel evidently contains I_T. Let ζ be the induced homomorphism of $T^{-1}R$ into S. It is obvious that $\eta = \zeta \circ \varphi_T$. If ϑ is any other homomorphism of

$T^{-1}R$ into S with $\eta = \vartheta \circ \varphi_T$, then ϑ induces a homomorphism $\vartheta' : R[(X_t)] \to S$. We then have

$$\vartheta'(X_t)\,\eta(t) = \vartheta(x_t)\,\vartheta(\varphi_T(t)) = \vartheta(x_t\,\varphi_T(t))$$
$$= \vartheta(1) = 1\ ,$$

where x_t is the I_T-residue of X_t. Thus $\vartheta'(X_t) = 1/\eta(t)$ as required.

COMPLEMENT 3.4. If R is a domain and T does not contain 0, then $T^{-1}R$ is canonically isomorphic to the subring of the fraction field of R consisting of elements of the form f/g, $f \in R$, $g \in T$.

PROPOSITION 3.5. If I is an ideal of $T^{-1}R$ and $I^c = \varphi_T^{-1} I$, then $I = I^c(T^{-1}R)$. In particular, if R is noetherian, then so is $T^{-1}R$.

Proof: The second assertion is immediate, granted the first, because if I^c is finitely generated, so is I. Now if we replace R by $R/\ker \varphi_T$, then we may assume that φ_T is injective, i.e., that $R \subset T^{-1}R$. Then $I^c = I \cap R$. Denote the image of X_t in $T^{-1}R$ by $1/t$. Then our proposition will follow if we show that for any $g \in T^{-1}R$, there exists a $t \in T$ such that $tg \in R$, for then I will be generated by elements of R. According to the definition, every element of $T^{-1}R$ can be written as a polynomial in the elements $1/t$, $t \in T$, with coefficients in R, from which everything follows by clearing denominators.

REMARK. If M is an R-module, we set $T^{-1}M = M \otimes_R T^{-1}R$. There are two cases of localization which are of paramount interest.

1. If $f \in R$, let $T = \{f^n : n > 0\}$. In this case one writes R_f for $T^{-1}R$. We have encountered this construction already when R is a domain and $f \neq 0$. Then we have $R_f = R[1/f]$.

2. Note that an ideal $\underline{p}$ of R is prime if and only if $R - \underline{p}$ is a multiplicative set in R. We denote $(R - \underline{p})^{-1}R$ in this case by $R_{\underline{p}}$ and call this ring the localization of R at $\underline{p}$.

DEFINITION 3.6. A <u>local ring</u> is a ring in which the non-units form an ideal. Note that if R is a local ring then the ideal of non-units is the unique maximal ideal of R.

DEFINITION 3.7. Let V be an affine algebraic set, and let v be a point of V. Let $\underline{o}_{V,v} = k[V]_{\underline{m}}$, where $\underline{m}$ is the maximal ideal in k[V] corresponding to v. $\underline{o}_{V,v}$ is called the <u>local ring of v on V</u>.

PROPOSITION 3.8. If V is an affine variety, then

$\underline{o}_{V,v}$ is the set of all elements of $k(V)$ of the form f/g, $f,g \in k[V]$, $g(v) \neq 0$.

Proof: This is immediate from complement 3.4.

PROPOSITION 3.9. (Nakayama's lemma) Let R be a local ring with maximal ideal $\underline{m}$ and let M be a finitely generated R-module. If $\underline{m}M = M$, then $M = (0)$.

Proof: If $M \neq (0)$, let $m_1,\ldots,m_r$ be a minimal set of generators for M over R. Then $\underline{m}M = M$ implies that

$$m_1 = \sum_{i=1}^{r} a_i m_i , \quad a_i \in \underline{m} .$$

Then

$$(1 - a_1)m_1 = \sum_{i=2}^{r} a_i m_i$$

and $1 - a_1$ is a unit of R since $a_1 \in \underline{m}$. Thus

$$m_1 = \sum_{i=2}^{r} \frac{a_i}{1 - a_1} m_i ,$$

contradicting the minimality. Therefore $M = (0)$.

PROPOSITION 3.10. Let R be a noetherian local ring and let K be the residue field $R/\underline{m}$. Then $\underline{m} \otimes_R K = \underline{m}/\underline{m}^2$ is a finite dimensional vector space over K and $\dim_K(\underline{m}/\underline{m}^2)$ is the cardinality of a minimal set of generators of $\underline{m}$. More specifically, if $f_1,\ldots,f_r \in \underline{m}$ then these elements generate $\underline{m}$ if and only if their residues mod $\underline{m}^2$ span $\underline{m}/\underline{m}^2$ and they form a minimal set of generators of $\underline{m}$ if and only if their residues mod $\underline{m}^2$ form a basis of $\underline{m}/\underline{m}^2$.

Proof: Since $\underline{m}$ is a finitely generated R-module, $\underline{m} \otimes_R K$ is a finitely generated K-module. Clearly the last assertion implies all the rest. Let $\bar{f}_i$ denote the $\underline{m}^2$-residue of f_i. Then $\bar{f}_1, \ldots, \bar{f}_r$ form a basis if and only if the K-linear mapping $K^r \to \underline{m}/\underline{m}^2$ given by $(0,\ldots,\overset{i}{1},\ldots,0) \mapsto \bar{f}_i$ is an isomorphism. But this mapping is induced from the R-homomorphism $R^r \xrightarrow{\varphi} \underline{m}$ defined by $(0,\ldots,\overset{i}{1},\ldots,0) \mapsto f_i$, by tensoring with K. If $M = \operatorname{coker} \varphi = \underline{m}/\varphi R^r$, then M is a finitely generated R-module and $M \otimes_R K = (0)$, whence $M = (0)$. Therefore φ is surjective if and only if $\varphi \otimes 1_K$ is surjective. Hence the $\bar{f}_i$ span $\underline{m}/\underline{m}^2$ if and only if the f_i generate $\underline{m}$. Moreover, e.g., if $f_1, \ldots, f_{r-1}$ generate $\underline{m}$ then $\bar{f}_1, \ldots, \bar{f}_{r-1}$ span $\underline{m}/\underline{m}^2$ so that the $\bar{f}_i$ form a basis if and only if the f_i form a minimal set of generators.

Now let V be an affine algebraic set and let W be a closed subset. Let I be the ideal of W in k[V]. If v is a point of W then $I\underline{o}_{V,v}$ is an ideal in $\underline{o}_{V,v}$ and $\underline{o}_{W,v} = \underline{o}_{V,v}/I\underline{o}_{V,v}$. This follows from the general fact that if R is a ring, T a multiplicative set in R, and I an ideal in R, then if T' denotes the image of T in

R/I, then $T^{-1}R/I(T^{-1}R)$ is canonically isomorphic to $T'^{-1}(R/I)$. This can be proved from the following general argument. Given an exact sequence

$$0 \longrightarrow M' \longrightarrow M \longrightarrow M'' \longrightarrow 0$$

of R-modules and R-homomorphisms, the sequence

$$0 \longrightarrow T^{-1}M' \rightarrow T^{-1}M \rightarrow T^{-1}M'' \longrightarrow 0$$

is exact. To prove this, by lemma 1.25, we need only show that $T^{-1}M' \rightarrow T^{-1}M$ is injective. If N is any R-module, set $T(N;0) = \{n \in N : tn = 0$ for some $t \in T\}$. Then we have an exact commutative diagram

$$\begin{array}{ccccccc} 0 & \rightarrow & T(M;0) & \rightarrow & M & \xrightarrow{u} & T^{-1}M \\ & & \uparrow & & \uparrow & & \uparrow \alpha \\ 0 & \rightarrow & T(M';0) & \rightarrow & M' & \xrightarrow{v} & T^{-1}M' \end{array} .$$

Since $T(M';0) = T(M;0) \cap M'$, we may replace M by $M/T(M;0)$, M' by $M'/T(M';0)$ and assume that u and v are injective, since $T^{-1}(M/T(M;0)) = T^{-1}M$, etc. If m' is a non-zero element of $T^{-1}M'$ such that $\alpha(m') = 0$ then we can find a unit $t \in T^{-1}R$ such that $tm' \in vM'$ and then $u(v^{-1}(tm')) = 0$ which is a contradiction.

III-2 DERIVATIONS AND LIE ALGEBRAS

DEFINITION 3.11. Let A be a k-algebra - which need not be commutative or even associative nor need it have an identity - and let B be a k-algebra containing A. A <u>k-derivation</u> of A into B is a k-linear mapping $D : A \to B$ such that $D(xy) = xDy + (Dx)y$ for all $x,y \in A$. We denote the set of all k-derivations of A into B by $\mathrm{Der}_k(A,B)$. We write $\mathrm{Der}_k(A)$ for $\mathrm{Der}_k(A,A)$.

EXERCISE. Show that if $D,D' \in \mathrm{Der}_k(A,B)$ then $aD + bD' \in \mathrm{Der}_k(A,B)$ for any $a,b \in k$ and hence that $\mathrm{Der}_k(A,B)$ is a vector space over k.

DEFINITION 3.12. A <u>Lie</u> <u>algebra</u> over k is a k-vector space L together with a bilinear mapping $[\ ,\ ] : L \times L \to L$ such that

i) $[x,y] + [y,x] = 0$ for all $x,y \in L$

ii) $[x,[y,z]] + [y,[z,x]] + [z,[x,y]] = 0$ for all $x,y,z \in L$.

(ii) is known as 'Jacobi's identity'.)

Perhaps the most immediate example of a Lie algebra over k is the following. Let L be an associative algebra over k and define $[x,y] = xy - yx$ for $x,y \in L$. It is a straightforward matter to verify that this 'bracket' gives a Lie algebra structure on L.

PROPOSITION 3.13. Let A be a k-algebra (as above).

If $D,E \in Der_k(A)$, let $[D,E] = DE - ED$. Then, with this bracket, $Der_k(A)$ is a Lie algebra over k.

Proof: We must first show that $[D,E] \in Der_k(A)$. That $[D,E]$ is k-linear is obvious, as is the bilinearity of the bracket. Now if $x,y \in A$, then

$$\begin{aligned}
[D,E](xy) &= (DE - ED)(xy) = DE(xy) - ED(xy) \\
&= D(xEy + (Ex)y) - E(xDy + (Dx)y) \\
&= xDEy + DxEy + ExDy + (DEx)y \\
&\quad - xEDy - ExDy - DxEy - (EDx)y \\
&= xDEy + (DEx)y - xEDy - (EDx)y \\
&= x[D,E]y + ([D,E]x)y .
\end{aligned}$$

i) is clear from the definition, so we need only check the Jacobi identity. If $D,E,F \in Der_k(A)$ then

$$\begin{aligned}
&[D,[E,F]] + [E,[F,D]] + [F,[D,E]] = \\
&[D,(EF - FE)] + [E,(FD - DF)] + [F,(DE - ED)] = \\
&D(EF - FE) - (EF - FE)D + E(FD - DF) \\
&\quad - (FD - DF)E + F(DE - ED) - (DE - ED)F = \\
&DEF - DFE - EFD + FED + EFD - EDF \\
&\quad - FDE + DFE + FDE - FED - DEF + EDF = 0.
\end{aligned}$$

DEFINITION 3.14. Let V be an affine algebraic set and let v be a point of V. By a <u>point derivation</u>

at v we mean a k-linear mapping $D : \underline{o}_{V,v} \rightarrow k$ such that $D(fg) = f(v)Dg + g(v)Df$ for all f,g.

Intuitively, a derivation $D : k[V] \rightarrow k[V]$ may be thought of as partial differentiation with respect to a suitable variable, whereas a point derivation may be thought of as partial differentiation followed by evaluation at a point. We denote the set of point derivations at $v \in V$ by $Der_{V,v}$. Clearly $Der_{V,v}$ is a k-vector space. Now we have the extremely important:

THEOREM 3.15. Let V be an affine algebraic set and let v be a point of V. Then $Der_{V,v}$ is canonically isomorphic to $(\underline{m}_v/\underline{m}_v^2)^*$ where $\underline{m}_v$ denotes the maximal ideal of $\underline{o}_{V,v}$.

<u>Proof</u>: First we note that if $D \in Der_{V,v}$ and $f \in \underline{m}_v^2$, then $Df = 0$. To see this, write $f = \sum g_i h_i$, with $g_i, h_i \in \underline{m}_v$. Then $D(g_i h_i) = g_i(v)Dh_i + h_i(v)Dg_i = 0$. Therefore, we can regard D as a k-linear map $\underline{o}_{V,v}/\underline{m}_v^2 \rightarrow k$. But $\underline{o}_{V,v}/\underline{m}_v^2$ is isomorphic as k-vector space to $k + \underline{m}_v/\underline{m}_v^2$. Now if $a \in k$, then $Da = D(a \cdot 1) = aD1 = aD(1 \cdot 1) = aD1 + aD1 = 2Da$ so that $Da = 0$. Thus D is trivial on k and therefore can be identified as an element of $(\underline{m}_v/\underline{m}_v^2)^*$.

Conversely, given $F \in (\underline{m}_v/\underline{m}_v^2)^*$, we define a point derivation at v by $Df = F(\overline{f})$ where $\overline{f}$

is the $\underline{m}_v^2$-residue of $f - f(v)$. Then D is clearly k-linear and:

$$D(fg) = F(\overline{fg}) = F(fg - f(v)g(v) \bmod \underline{m}_v^2) =$$

$$F((f - f(v))(g - g(v)) + f(v)g + g(v)f - 2f(v)g(v) \bmod \underline{m}_v^2)$$

$$= F(f(v)g + g(v)f - 2f(v)g(v) \bmod \underline{m}_v^2)$$

$$= F(f(v)(g - g(v)) + g(v)(f - f(v)) \bmod \underline{m}_v^2)$$

$$= f(v)F(\overline{g}) + g(v)F(\overline{f}) = f(v)Dg + g(v)Df.$$

REMARK. The vector space $(\underline{m}_v/\underline{m}_v^2)^*$ can be interpreted as the space of tangent vectors to V at v as follows. We embed V in $\underline{A}^n$ and regard $\underline{A}^n$ as a vector space over k. Then the vector $\underline{a} = (a_1, \ldots, a_n)$ is tangent to V at v if - setting $F_{\underline{a}}(t) = f(v + t\underline{a})$ - we have $F'_{\underline{a}}(0) = 0$, for all $f \in \underline{I}_{\underline{A}^n}(V)$. Moreover

$$F'_{\underline{a}}(t) = \sum_i \frac{\partial f}{\partial X_i}(t)\frac{dX_i}{dt} = \sum_i a_i \frac{\partial f}{\partial X_i} .$$

Thus $\underline{a}$ is tangent to V at v if the derivation $D_{\underline{a}} = \sum a_i(\partial/\partial X_i)$ of $k[\underline{A}^n]$ maps $\underline{I}(V)$ into $\underline{I}(\{v\})$. Such a derivation then induces a point derivation of $\underline{o}_{V,v}$ into k, and conversely. Denoting the space of vectors tangent to V at v by $T_v(V)$, we then have canonical isomorphisms of vector spaces

$$T_v(V) \approx \mathrm{Der}_{V,v} \approx (\underline{m}_v/\underline{m}_v^2)^* .$$

III-3 THE LIE ALGEBRA OF AN AFFINE GROUP

DEFINITION 3.16. Let G be an affine group. We say that $D \in \mathrm{Der}_k(k[G])$ is invariant if $D(f^x) = (Df)^x$ for all $f \in k[G]$ and all $x \in G$.

PROPOSITION 3.17. The set $\mathrm{Der}_k(k[G])^G$ of invariant derivations of $k[G]$ is a Lie subalgebra of $\mathrm{Der}_k(k[G])$.

Proof: That it is a subspace over k is evident. Now if $D,E \in \mathrm{Der}_k(k[G])^G$ and $f \in k[G]$, $x \in G$, then

$$[D,E](f^x) = (DE - ED)(f^x) = DE(f^x) - ED(f^x)$$

$$= (DEf)^x - (EDf)^x = ([D,E]f)^x .$$

If $D \in \mathrm{Der}_k(k[G])$ and G is connected, then we can extend D to a derivation of $k(G)$ by setting $D(f/g) = (gDf - fDg)/g^2$ in the usual way. If $f \in \underline{o}_{G,e}$ and $D \in \mathrm{Der}_k(k[G])^G$, we set $D_e(f) = Df(e)$. Then D_e is a point derivation at e and the map $D \mapsto D_e$ is a k-linear mapping of $\mathrm{Der}_k(k[G])$ into $\mathrm{Der}_{G,e}$.

PROPOSITION 3.18. $D \mapsto D_e$ is a k-isomorphism of $\mathrm{Der}_k(k[G])^G$ onto $\mathrm{Der}_{G,e}$.

Proof: If D is invariant, then $Df(x) = (Df)^x(e) = D(f^x)(e) = 0$ for all f implies $D_e = 0$ so that the map is injective. If $X \in \mathrm{Der}_{G,e}$, let $(D_X f)(x) = X(f^x)$ for all $f \in k[G]$. To show that $D_X f \in k[G]$, let $\tilde{m}(f) = \sum h_i \otimes g_i$. Then $f^x = \sum h_i(x) g_i$ so that $(D_X f)(x) = \sum h_i(x) X(g_i)$, i.e., $D_X f = \sum X(g_i) h_i \in k[G]$. Also,

$$(D_X(f^y))(x) = X((f^y)^x) = X(f^{xy}) = (D_X f)(xy)$$
$$= (D_X f)^y(x).$$

Thus D_X is invariant. Finally, $(D_X)_e = X$.

Thus for a connected affine group we have <u>four</u> canonically isomorphic vector spaces:

$$T_e(G) \approx (\underline{m}_e/\underline{m}_e^2)^* \approx \mathrm{Der}_{G,e} \approx \mathrm{Der}_k(k[G])^G .$$

The last is a Lie algebra and we can define Lie algebra structures on each of the others via the canonical isomorphisms.

DEFINITION 3.19. If G is a connected affine group we denote by $\underline{g}$ the Lie algebra above. If G is not connected $\underline{g}$ denotes the Lie algebra attached to the connected component of the identity, G_o. $\underline{g}$ is called the <u>Lie algebra of</u> $\underline{G}$. As a matter of notation, we will use the same letter, lower case and underlined, to denote the Lie algebra of a group as that used, upper case, to denote the group.

If $\varphi : V \to W$ is a k-morphism of affine algebraic sets and $v \in V$, let $w = \varphi(v)$. Then the homomorphism $\tilde{\varphi}: k[W] \to k[V]$ induces a homomorphism of local rings $\tilde{\varphi}_v : \underline{o}_{W,w} \to \underline{o}_{V,v}$, viz., $\tilde{\varphi}_v(f/g) = \tilde{\varphi} f/\tilde{\varphi} g$, for $f \in k[W]$, $g \in k[W]$, $g(w) \neq 0$. Note that $\tilde{\varphi}_v$ takes the maximal ideal of $\underline{o}_{W,w}$ into the maximal ideal of $\underline{o}_{V,v}$, as $f(w) = 0$ implies that $\tilde{\varphi} f(v) = 0$. $\tilde{\varphi}_v$ also takes units of $\underline{o}_{W,w}$ to units of $\underline{o}_{V,v}$.

Now if $\varphi: G \to G'$ is a k-homomorphism of affine groups, then $\tilde{\varphi}_e$ takes $\underline{o}_{G',e'}$ to $\underline{o}_{G,e}$. If $X \in \underline{g}$, then $X \circ \tilde{\varphi}_e \in \underline{g}'$ and it is easily seen that $X \mapsto X \circ \tilde{\varphi}_e$ is a k-linear mapping. We denote this mapping of $\underline{g}$ into $\underline{g}'$ by $d\varphi_e$ or simply by $d\varphi$.

THEOREM 3.20. Let $\varphi: G \to G'$ be a k-homomorphism of affine groups. Then $d\varphi_e$ is a homomorphism of Lie algebras, i.e., $d\varphi[X,Y] = [d\varphi X, d\varphi Y]$, for all $X, Y \in \underline{g}$.

Proof: If $f \in k[G']$ and $X, Y \in \underline{g}$, then:

$$[d\varphi X, d\varphi Y]f = [D_{d\varphi X}, D_{d\varphi Y}]f(e') =$$
$$(D_{d\varphi X}D_{d\varphi Y} - D_{d\varphi Y}D_{d\varphi X})f(e') =$$
$$(D_{d\varphi X}D_{d\varphi Y}f - D_{d\varphi Y}D_{d\varphi X}f)(e').$$

$$d\varphi[X,Y]f = ([X,Y] \circ \tilde{\varphi}_e)f = ([D_X, D_Y]_e \circ \tilde{\varphi}_e)f =$$
$$[D_X, D_Y]_e(f \circ \varphi) = [D_X, D_Y](f \circ \varphi)(e) =$$

$$(D_X D_Y - D_Y D_X)(f\circ\varphi)(e) =$$

$$(D_X D_Y(f\circ\varphi) - D_Y D_X(f\circ\varphi))(e).$$

But $D_X(f\circ\varphi)(e) = X(f\circ\varphi)$ and

$$D_{d\varphi X}f(y) = d\varphi X(f^y) = (X\circ\widetilde{\varphi}_e)f^y = X(f^y\circ\varphi),$$

for all $y \in G'$. Therefore

$$D_{d\varphi Y}D_{d\varphi X}f(e') = d\varphi Y(D_{d\varphi X}f) = Y((D_{d\varphi X}f)\circ\varphi),$$

and $D_Y D_X(f\circ\varphi)(e) = Y(D_X(f\circ\varphi))$. We will clearly be finished if we show that $D_X(f\circ\varphi) = (D_{d\varphi X}f)\circ\varphi$. But

$$((D_{d\varphi X}f)\circ\varphi)(x) = d\varphi X(f^{\varphi x}) = X(f^{\varphi x}\circ\varphi),$$

and $D_X(f\circ\varphi)(x) = X((f\circ\varphi)^x)$. Consequently, it suffices to show that $f^{\varphi x}\circ\varphi = (f\circ\varphi)^x$ for any $x \in G$. However, if $y \in G$, then

$$(f\circ\varphi)^x(y) = (f\circ\varphi)(yx) = f(\varphi y\varphi x) =$$

$$f^{\varphi x}(\varphi y) = (f^{\varphi x}\circ\varphi)(y). \qquad \text{q.e.d.}$$

This indicates that there is more than a casual connection between an affine group and its Lie algebra - that the structure of the Lie algebra ought to reflect the structure of the group. The remainder of the chapter will be devoted to examining the relation between an affine group and its Lie algebra.

PROPOSITION 3.21. If G is an affine group and G'

is a closed subgroup of G, let $\iota : G' \to G$ be the inclusion homomorphism. Then $d\iota : \underline{g}' \to \underline{g}$ is injective.

Proof: Since $\tilde{\iota} : k[G] \to k[G']$ is surjective, it follows that $\tilde{\iota}_{e'} : \underline{o}_{G,e} \to \underline{o}_{G',e'}$ is surjective. If $X \in \underline{g}'$, then $d\iota X = X \circ \tilde{\iota}_{e'}$ so $d\iota$ is injective.

If $\psi : G \to G'$ is a surjective k-homomorphism of affine groups, it need not be true that $d\psi$ is surjective. For example, consider the homomorphism $x \mapsto x^p$ of G_a into G_a in characteristic $p > 0$. Since k is algebraically closed, this mapping is surjective, and is a k-homomorphism since it is given by $X \mapsto X^p$, $X \in k[X] = k[G_a]$. However, the corresponding Lie algebra homomorphism is identically zero, for $D(X^p) = pD(X^{p-1}) = 0$.

Let us look more closely at the Lie algebra $\underline{gl}_n$ of GL_n. We will need to know the explicit structure of this algebra later. We now show that there is a canonical isomorphism between $\underline{gl}_n$ and $M_n(k)$, the algebra of matrices of degree n over k, the latter algebra having the bracket $[X,Y] = XY - YX$. If X_{ij}, $1 \leq i,j \leq n$ are coordinates on $\underline{A}^{n^2}$, set $Y_{ij} = X_{ij} - \delta_{ij}$ (δ_{ij} = Kronecker 'delta', viz., $\delta_{ii} = 1$, $\delta_{ij} = 0$, for $i \neq j$.) Then the identity $1 \in GL_n$ is the origin of the Y-coordinates. If

$\underline{o} = \underline{o}_{GL_n,1}$ and $\underline{m} = \underline{m}_1$ is the maximal ideal of $\underline{o}$ then $\underline{m}$ is generated by the Y_{ij} and these form a minimal ideal basis, i.e., their $\underline{m}^2$-residues form a basis for $\underline{m}/\underline{m}^2$. Thus if $X \in \underline{gl}_n$ then $X \mapsto (X(Y_{ij}))$ gives a bijective k-linear mapping from $\underline{gl}_n$ to $M_n(k)$.

What does the bracket look like? If $X \in \underline{gl}_n$ then

$$D_X(Y_{ij})(x) = D_X(Y_{ij})^x(1) = X(Y_{ij}^x) ,$$

for $x \in GL_n$. Regarding $X(Y_{ij}^x)$ as a k-valued function on GL_n we have

$$Y(X(Y_{ij}^x)) = Y(D_X(Y_{ij})^x) = D_Y(D_X(Y_{ij}))(x) ,$$

from which we see that $[X,Y] = XY - YX$, X and Y being regarded as matrices.

EXERCISE. Show that the Lie algebra $\underline{sl}_n$ of SL_n can be identified as the subalgebra of $\underline{gl}_n$ consisting of matrices of trace 0.

III-4 DIMENSION THEORY

We recall that if L is an extension of a field K then L is said to be <u>separably generated</u>, or simply <u>separable</u>, over K if there exists a transcendence basis (u) of L over K such that L is a separable algebraic extension of $K(u)$. Such a transcendence basis is called a separating transcendence basis for L over K. Whether or not L is separable over K depends, so to speak, on how K is embedded in L. We shall not enter into a detailed discussion of these matters here.

If $\varphi : V \to W$ is a k-morphism of affine varieties such that $\overline{\varphi V} = W$, we say that φ is a separable morphism if $k(V)$ is a separable extension of $\tilde{\varphi} k(W)$. Since k is algebraically closed, any extension of k is separable over k. To see this in the case of a finitely generated extension L of k, assume first that $L = k(x)$. Then either $x \in k$ or x is transcendental over k. In both cases, L is separable over k. Now let $L = k(x_1,\ldots,x_n)$. If $x_1,\ldots,x_r$ is a transcendence basis for L over k, let $f(X_1,\ldots,X_r,X_{r+1})$ $k[X_1,\ldots,X_r,X_{r+1}]$ be a polynomial of minimum degree such that $f(x_1,\ldots,x_r,x_{r+1}) = 0$. If we have

$$f(X_1,\ldots,X_r,X_{r+1}) = g(X_1^p,\ldots,X_r^p,X_{r+1}^p),$$

where $p > 0$ is the characteristic, let g_o be the polynomial whose coefficients are the p-th roots of the coefficients of g. Then $g_o(x_1,\ldots,x_r,x_{r+1}) = 0$ and g_o has smaller degree than f. Therefore, not all X_i can appear to the p-th power in f. Suppose that X_1 does not appear to the p-th power. Then x_1 is separable algebraic over $k(x_2,\ldots,x_{r+1})$ and hence over $k(x_2,\ldots,x_n)$. Thus we need only show that $k(x_2,\ldots,x_n)$ is separable over k, and we can finish by induction.

DEFINITION 3.22. If V is an affine variety, we denote by $\dim_k V$, or simply $\dim V$, the transcendence degree of $k(V)$ over k. If V is an affine algebraic set, we let $\dim V = \max(\dim V_i)$, the V_i being the irreducible components of V.

The notion of dimension is a fairly intuitive one, but, as with many such 'obvious' concepts, it turns out to be a difficult task, except in the simplest cases, to make it into a workable mathematical tool. Our treatment of dimension will be a compromise - the definition of dimension that we have given is a purely algebraic, i.e., non-topological, one. It will be quite adequate for our purposes, but it does bypass the really hard problem of making a connection with intuition. Our main objective in this section is to show that the dimension of an affine group is the same as the dimension of its Lie algebra - regarded as a vector space over k.

The following lemma is a weak version of the so-called Noether normalization lemma (which we will prove in chapter V).

LEMMA 3.23. Let V be an affine variety, v a

point of V, and $\underline{m}$ the maximal ideal of $\underline{o}_{V,v}$. Then there exist elements $f_1,\ldots,f_r \in k[V]$ such that:

i) $f_1,\ldots,f_r$ form a minimal ideal basis of $\underline{m}$.

ii) For some $t \leqslant r$, $f_1,\ldots,f_t$ form a transcendence basis of $k(V)$ over k.

Proof: We may assume that $V \subset \underline{A}^n$ and that $v = o$ is the origin of $\underline{A}^n$. If $k[V] = k[f_1,\ldots,f_n]$ then $f_1,\ldots,f_n$ generate $\underline{m}$ and we may assume that $f_1,\ldots,f_r$ form a minimal basis of this ideal. If I is the ideal in $k[V]$ generated by $f_1,\ldots,f_r$ and $W = \underline{V}_V(I)$, then $W = \{o\} \cup W'$ with W' closed in V and $o \notin W'$. To see this, let W_o be an irreducible component of W containing o. Then $\underline{o}_{W_o,o}$ is a homomorphic image of $\underline{o}_{V,o}/I\underline{o}_{V,o} = k$. Therefore $\underline{o}_{W_o,o} = k$. But $k[W_o] \subset \underline{o}_{W_o,o}$ so that $k[W_o] = k$. Thus $W_o = \{o\}$.

Replacing V by V_g for a suitable $g \in k[V]$ such that $g(o) \neq 0$, we may assume that $f_1,\ldots,f_r$ vanish together on V only at the origin, and that $f_n = 1/g$, since adjoining $1/g$ to $k[V]$ does not change the structure of $\underline{o}_{V,o}$, as g is a unit in this ring.

Now, for each i, $r+1 \leqslant i \leqslant n$, the inclusion $k[f_1,\ldots,f_r,f_i] \subset k[f_1,\ldots,f_n]$ induces a k-morphism $\varphi_i : V \to V_i$, where V_i is the affine model of

$k[f_1,\ldots,f_r,f_i]$. If W_i is the locus of $(f_1,\ldots,f_r)$ on V_i, then $\varphi_i^{-1}W_i = \{o\}$ so $f_1,\ldots,f_r$ vanish together on V_i only at the origin. Then, according to the nullstellensatz, in $k[V_i]$ we have $(f_1,\ldots,f_r,f_i)^{m_i} \subset (f_1,\ldots,f_r)$ for a suitable integer, m_i. In particular, we have $f_i^{m_i} \in (f_1,\ldots,f_r)$. This means that there is a relation of the form $F(f_1,\ldots,f_r,f_i) = 0$, with $0 \neq F \in k[X_1,\ldots,X_r,X_i]$. Thus $f_1,\ldots,f_r,f_i$ are algebraically dependent over k and so f_i is algebraic over $k(f_1,\ldots,f_r)$, $r + 1 \leqslant i \leqslant n$. Therefore $k(V)$ is algebraic over $k(f_1,\ldots,f_r)$ and we can choose a transcendence basis for $k(V)$ over k from among the elements $f_1,\ldots,f_r$. q.e.d.

COROLLARY 3.24. If V is an affine variety, then for all $v \in V$, $\dim T_v(V) \geqslant \dim V$.

DEFINITION 3.25. If V is an affine variety and v is a point of V, we say that V is smooth at v if $\dim T_v(V) = \dim V$. If V is an affine algebraic set, we say that V is smooth at $v \in V$ if v belongs to exactly one irreducible component V_o of V and V_o is smooth at v.

Our next objective is to show that the points of an affine algebraic set V at which V is smooth form a non-empty open subset of V.

Let K be an extension field of k. If $F = \sum a_i X^i \in K[X]$ and $D \in \mathrm{Der}_k(K)$, let $F^D = \sum D(a_i)X^i$. Now if $L = K(x_1,\ldots,x_n)$ is a finitely generated extension of K and $G \in K[X_1,\ldots,X_n]$, let $G_{X_i} = \frac{\partial G}{\partial X_i}$ and let $G_{x_i} = G_{X_i}(x_1,\ldots,x_n)$. If $G(x_1,\ldots,x_n) = 0$ then

$$D(G(x_1,\ldots,x_n)) = G^D(x_1,\ldots,x_n) + \sum_{i=1}^{n} G_{x_i} D'(x_i) = 0,$$

for any $D' \in \mathrm{Der}_k(L)$ which extends D. We then have the following converse to this fact.

LEMMA 3.26. Let K be an extension of k and let $\underline{p} = (f_1,\ldots,f_r)$ be a prime ideal in $K[X_1,\ldots,X_n]$. Let x_i denote the $\underline{p}$-residue of X_i and let $D \in \mathrm{Der}_k(K)$. If $u_1,\ldots,u_n$ are elements of $K(x_1,\ldots,x_n)$ such that

$$f_j^D(x_1,\ldots,x_n) + \sum_{i=1}^{n} (f_j)_{x_i} u_i = 0 , \quad 1 \leqslant j \leqslant n,$$

then there is a unique $E \in \mathrm{Der}_k(K(x_1,\ldots,x_n))$ such that E extends D and $Ex_i = u_i$.

<u>Proof</u>: First note that if $f,g \in K[x_1,\ldots,x_n]$, $g \neq 0$, then if we set $Ef = f^D + \sum f_{x_i} u_i$ and $E(f/g) = (gEf - fEg)/g^2$, then E is a k-derivation of $K(x_1,\ldots,x_n)$. Now, proceeding step by step, we may assume that $n = 1$. Then if $x = x_1$ is transcendental over K, D extends to $K(x)$ and $u = u_1$ may

be selected arbitrarily. If x is separably algebraic over K, let F be its monic minimal polynomial over K. Then $F' \neq 0$ and $F^D(x) + F'(x)u = 0$ so we must have $u = -F^D(x)/F'(x)$. If x is purely inseparable over K, then $x^{p^n} - a = 0$, for some n and some $a \in K$. Then D extends to $K(x)$ if and only if $Da = 0$.

THEOREM 3.27. Let V be an affine algebraic set. Then the set of points of V at which V is smooth form a non-empty open subset of V.

Proof: Clearly we may assume that V is an affine variety, and that $V \subset \underline{A}^n$. Let $I = \underline{I}_{\underline{A}^n}(V) = (f_1,\ldots,f_r)$.

Step 1. We show that if v is a point of V, then $\dim T_v(V) = n - \text{rank}((f_i)_{x_j})$, where $v = (x_1,\ldots,x_n)$. There is no loss of generality in assuming that v is the origin. Let $\underline{M}$ be the maximal ideal of the origin in $\underline{A}^n$ and $\underline{m}$ the maximal ideal of the origin on V. Then the exact sequence

$$\underline{M}/\underline{M}^2 \to \underline{m}/\underline{m}^2 \to 0$$

yields an exact sequence

$$0 \to T_o(V) \xrightarrow{\vartheta} T_o(\underline{A}^n).$$

Since $T_o(\underline{A}^n) = \underline{A}^n$, it suffices to show that the rank of ϑ is the rank of $((f_i)_{x_j})_{x_1=x_2=\cdots=x_n=0}$.

If $f_i = \sum a_{ij} X_j + \sum a_{ijp} X_j X_p + \cdots$, then

$$((f_i)_{x_j})_{x_1 = \cdots = x_n = 0} = (a_{ij}) ,$$

so that the rank of the matrix on the left hand side is $\dim((I + \underline{M}^2)/\underline{M}^2)$ as required.

This shows that the points at which V is smooth are just those at which the matrix $((f_i)_{x_j})$ has rank $n - \dim V$. Using corollary 3.24, we see that the set of these points is open, since it is the complement on V of the locus of the set of minor determinants of $((f_i)_{x_j})$ of order $n - \dim V$.

Step 2. We show that this open set is non-empty. For this, it evidently suffices to show that the matrix $((f_i)_{x_j})$ - regarded as a matrix over $k(V)$ - has rank $n - \dim V$. But the nullity of this matrix is precisely the dimension of the subspace of $k(V)^n$ consisting of those n-tuples $(u_1, \ldots, u_n)$ such that $\sum (f_i)_{x_j} u_j = 0$. By lemma 3.26, this is the dimension of $\mathrm{Der}_k(k(V))$ as a module over $k(V)$. By the same lemma, this is the transcendence degree of $k(V)$ over k, i.e., the dimension of V.

COROLLARY 3.28. If G is an affine group, then $\dim G = \dim \underline{g}$.

Proof: Since G is a group, all the local rings of points of G are isomorphic, since $x \mapsto yx$

is a k-automorphism of the algebraic set G. Since G has at least one point at which it is smooth, it follows that G is smooth at each of its points. In particular, G is smooth at e and the corollary follows.

III-5 FUNCTORIAL PROPERTIES OF THE LIE ALGEBRA

We have already seen that if H is a closed subgroup of the affine group G, then

$$\underline{h} = \{X \in \underline{g} : Xf = 0 \text{ for all } f \in \underline{I}_G(H)\underline{o}_{G,e}\}.$$

Thus if $\varphi : G' \to G$ is a k-isomorphism of G' onto a closed subgroup of G, then $(d\varphi^{-1})\underline{h}$ is the Lie algebra of $\varphi^{-1}H$, for if $X \in \underline{g}'$ then X annihilates $(\tilde{\varphi}\,\underline{I}_G(H))k[G']$ if and only if $d\varphi X$ annihilates $\underline{I}_G(H)$.

Now let $P \subset N \subset M = \underline{A}^n$ be linear subspaces. Let

$$GL(P,N) = \{x \in GL_n : xm \equiv m \bmod P, \text{ for all } m \in N\}.$$

Then GL(P,N) is a closed subgroup of GL_n. If $\chi \in (M/P)^*$ then $u \mapsto \chi(um)$, $m \in N$, is a linear form on $M_n(k)$, and

$$GL(P,N) =$$

$$\{x \in GL_n : \chi(xm) - \chi(m) = 0 \text{ for all } (\chi,m) \in (M/P)^* \times N\}.$$

The ideal of $GL(P,N)$ in $k[GL_n]$ is therefore generated by the functions $f_{\chi,m}$, where $f_{\chi,m}(x) = \chi(xm) - \chi(m)$, $\chi \in (M/P)^*$, $m \in N$. Thus $X \in \underline{gl}_n$ is in the Lie algebra $\underline{gl}(P,N)$ of $GL(P,N)$ if and only if X annihilates all such $f_{\chi,m}$, i.e.,

$$X(f_{\chi,m}) = D_X f_{\chi,m}(e) = \chi(Xm) = 0,$$

for all $(\chi,m) \in (M/P)^* \times N$. But this holds if and only if $XN \subset P$. Therefore

$$\underline{gl}(P,N) = \{X \in \underline{gl}_n : XN \subset P\}.$$

Now suppose that m is a fixed element of M and let G be the stabilizer of m in GL_n. Then

$$G = \{x \in GL_n : f_{\chi,m}(x) = 0 \text{ for all } \chi \in M^*\}.$$

Thus if $X \in \underline{gl}_n$ then X lies in $\underline{g}$ if and only if $\chi(Xm) = 0$ for all χ M^*. Therefore

$$\underline{g} = \{X \in \underline{gl}_n : Xm = 0\}.$$

Now let G be a connected affine group. Then $Der_k(k(G))$ is a $k(G)$-module. G acts on $k(G)$ via $(f/g)^x = f^x/g^x$, $f,g \in k[G]$, $x \in G$. We denote by $Der_k(k(G))^G$ the set of invariant elements of $Der_k(k(G))$, i.e., those D such that $(Df)^x = D(f^x)$ for all $f \in k(G)$, $x \in G$. If $D \in Der_k(k(G))^G$, we define, for any $x \in G$, $D_x \in T_x(G)$ by $D_x f = Df(x)$, $f \in \underline{o}_{G,x}$. Then, just as in proposition 3.18, the mapping $D \mapsto D_e$ is a k-isomorphism of $Der_k(k(G))^G$

onto $T_e(G) = \underline{g}$. We note that $f \in \underline{o}_{G,e}$ implies $Df \in \underline{o}_{G,e}$, for if $f = g/h$, $g,h \in k[G]$, $h(e) \neq 0$, then $Df = (hDg - gDh)/h^2$, which shows what we want.

EXERCISE. Show that $\mathrm{Der}_k(k(G)) = \mathrm{Der}_k(k(G))^G \otimes_k k(G)$.

THEOREM 3.29. Let G, G', and N be affine groups and let

$$(1) \rightarrow N \xrightarrow{\varphi} G \xrightarrow{\psi} G' \rightarrow (1)$$

be an exact sequence of k-homomorphisms, i.e., ψ is surjective, φ is injective, and $\varphi N = \ker \psi$. If ψ is separable, then the sequence

$$0 \rightarrow \underline{n} \xrightarrow{d\varphi} \underline{g} \xrightarrow{d\psi} \underline{g}' \rightarrow 0$$

of Lie algebras and Lie homomorphisms is exact.

Proof: Clearly we may assume that G and N are connected, whence G' is connected. First we show that $d\psi$ is surjective. To do this, we identify $\underline{g}$ and $\underline{g}'$ with $\mathrm{Der}_k(k(G))^G$ and $\mathrm{Der}_k(k(G'))^{G'}$, respectively. Since ψ is separable, G' is k-isomorphic to G/N so that we may identify $k(G')$ with $k(G)^N$. Then $\mathrm{Der}_k(k(G'))^{G'} = \mathrm{Der}_k(k(G'))^G$. Thus we must show that every G-invariant derivation of $k(G')$ can be extended to a G-invariant derivation of $k(G)$.

Let $z_1,\ldots,z_r$ be a transcendence basis for $k(G)$ over $k(G')$. Extend each $D \in \mathrm{Der}_k(k(G'))^G$ to $k(G')(z)$ by setting $Dz_i = 0$. Then every such extension extends uniquely to $k(G)$, by lemma 3.26. To show that this yields G-invariant extensions, let $f \in k(G)$ and let $F(f,z) = F(f,z_1,\ldots,z_r) = 0$ be a dependence relation, $F \in k(G')[X,X_1,\ldots,X_r]$. Then we must have

$$F^D(f,z) + Df\cdot F_X(f,z) + \sum_{i=1}^{r} Dz_i\cdot F_{X_i}(f,z) = 0.$$

As $Dz_i = 0$, for all i, this comes down to $Df = -F^D(f,z)/F_X(f,z)$. To see that D is invariant, we have

$$\begin{aligned}(Df)^x &= -(F^D)^x(f^x,z^x)/(F_X)^x(f^x,z^x)\\ &= -(F^x)^D(f^x,z^x)/(F^x)_X(f^x,z^x) = D(f^x),\end{aligned}$$

since $D|k(G')$ is G-invariant and so $(F^D)^x = (F^x)^D$ and $(F^x)_X = (F_X)^x$. Therefore $d\psi$ is surjective.

To see that $d\varphi\,\underline{n} = \ker(d\psi)$, we note that if $I' = \underline{I}_{G'}(\{e'\})$, then $I'k[G] \subset \underline{I}_G(N)$, whence the subalgebra L of $\underline{g}$ annihilating $I'k[G]$ contains $d\varphi\,\underline{n}$ and L is the kernel of $d\psi$. On the other hand, $\underline{V}_G(I'k[G]) = N$ so that $\underline{I}_G(N)^m \subset I'k[G]$, for m sufficiently large. Now if m is prime to the characteristic, then $D(f^m) = 0$ implies $Df = 0$, as $D(f^m) = mf^{m-1}Df$. Thus $L = d\varphi\,\underline{n}$. q.e.d.

COROLLARY 3.30. In the situation of theorem 3.29, we have $\dim G = \dim G' + \dim N$.

Proof: $\dim \underline{g} = \dim \underline{g}' + \dim \underline{n}$ and the corollary follows from corollary 3.28.

REMARK. The dimension relation of 3.30 holds even without the assumption that ψ is separable, but one cannot use the Lie algebras to prove it - one must use techniques which we shall not touch upon here, viz., formal power series.

Let G be a connected affine group and let M be a finite dimensional rational G-module. Then there is a homomorphism of Lie algebras $\underline{g} \to \underline{gl}(M)$ induced by the k-homomorphism $G \xrightarrow{\rho} GL(M)$. Suppose that N is a G-submodule of M. Then evidently $\underline{g}N \subset N$, since $\rho^{-1}GL(N,N) = G$ and $(d\rho)^{-1}\underline{gl}(N,N) = \underline{g}$. On the other hand if N is a $\underline{g}$-submodule of M, i.e., $XN \subset N$ for all X $\underline{g}$, then one may ask whether N is a G-submodule. Unfortunately, if the characteristic of k is $p > 0$, the answer may be negative as the following example shows.

Let G_a act on $M = \underline{A}^2$ by $(x,y) \mapsto (x, y + z^p)$, $z \in G_a$. Then since $\underline{g}_a$ must act trivially on M, i.e., $\underline{g}_a M = (0)$, every subspace of M is a $\underline{g}_a$-submodule. However, e.g., the diagonal subspace is not a G_a-submodule.

In the case where k has characteristic 0, the situation is much better.

PROPOSITION 3.31. Let G be a connected affine

group and let M be a finite dimensional rational G-module. If k has characteristic zero and N is a subspace of M, then $\underline{g}N \subset N$ if and only if N is a G-submodule of M.

Proof: If $\rho : G \to GL(M)$ is the given representation, let $H = \rho^{-1}GL(N,N)$. If $L = (d\rho)^{-1}\underline{gl}(N,N)$, then, setting $G' = GL(N,N) \cap \rho G$, the exact sequence

$$0 \to \ker(d\rho) \to \underline{h} \to \underline{g}' \to 0$$

shows that $L = \underline{h}$. Now N is a G-submodule of M if and only if $H = G$. But as $\dim H = \dim \underline{h}$, this is true if and only if $\underline{h} = \underline{g}$, i.e., if and only if $\underline{g}N \subset N$.

We conclude this section by examining the relation between closed normal subgroups of an affine group G and ideals in $\underline{g}$.

DEFINITION 3.32. If L is a Lie algebra over k, a subspace M of L is an ideal in L if and only if $[L,M] \subset M$, i.e., $X \in L$, $Y \in M$ implies $[X,Y] \in M$.

EXERCISE. Show that if M is an ideal in L, then L/M becomes a Lie algebra when we define the bracket by $[X + M, Y + M] = [X,Y] + M$, and that there is a canonical surjective Lie homomorphism from L to L/M.

Let A be a finite dimensional associative k-algebra with identity. A need not be commutative, e.g., $A = M_n(k)$. We may regard A as an affine variety, viz., $A = \underline{A}^n$, $n = \dim A$. Then the multiplication $m : A \times A \to A$ is a k-morphism, and U(A), the group of units of A, is, in a natural way, an affine group, in fact a closed subgroup of GL(A). The Lie algebra $\underline{u}(A)$ of U(A) is canonically isomorphic to A, where the bracket in A is the usual one, $[x,y] = xy - yx$.

EXERCISE. Verify that U(A) is a closed subgroup of GL(A). Show also that $\underline{u}(A)$ is Lie-isomorphic to A. (The proof follows the lines of that given before in the case $A = M_n(k)$.)

If G is any affine group, let $a_x(y) = xyx^{-1}$, $x,y \in G$. Then a_x is a k-automorphism of G. I claim that da_x is an automorphism of the Lie algebra $\underline{g}$. This follows from the general:

LEMMA 3.33. Let G, G', and G" be affine groups and let $\varphi : G \to G'$, $\psi : G' \to G''$ be k-homomorphisms. Then $d(\psi \circ \varphi) = d\psi \circ d\varphi$.

<u>Proof</u>: If $f'' \in k[G'']$, then $\widetilde{(\psi \circ \varphi)}_e(f'')$ = $f'' \circ (\psi \circ \varphi)_e = \tilde{\varphi}_e(\tilde{\psi}_{e'}(f''))$, whence $\widetilde{(\psi \circ \varphi)}_e$ = $\tilde{\varphi}_e \circ \tilde{\psi}_{e'}$. Now if $X \in \underline{g}''$, then

$$d(\psi \circ \varphi)X = X \circ (\widetilde{\psi \circ \varphi})_e = X \circ \tilde{\varphi}_e \circ \tilde{\psi}_{e'} = d\psi(d\varphi X).$$

Since the group $\mathrm{Aut}(\underline{g})$ of automorphisms of the Lie algebra $\underline{g}$ of G is evidently a closed subgroup of $GL(\underline{g})$, viz., the stabilizer of $[\ ,\ ] \in \underline{g}^* \otimes \underline{g}^* \otimes \underline{g}$, we obtain a k-homomorphism,

$$\mathrm{Ad} : G \to \mathrm{Aut}(\underline{g}),$$

defined by $\mathrm{Ad}(x) = da_x$. Ad is called the <u>adjoint</u> representation of G.

If L is any Lie algebra, we define a Lie homomorphism $\mathrm{ad}: L \to \mathrm{Der}_k(L)$ by $\mathrm{ad}(X)(Y) = [X,Y]$. This homomorphism is called the <u>adjoint</u> representation of L.

EXERCISE. Use Jacobi's identity to verify that ad is indeed a Lie homomorphism.

PROPOSITION 3.34. If G is an affine group, then $d(\mathrm{Ad}) = \mathrm{ad}$.

<u>Proof</u>: If we know the result in the case where $G = U(A)$, A a finite dimensional associative k-algebra with identity, which includes the case $G = GL_n$, then it follows for general G, for if $G \subset U(A)$, then $\underline{g} \subset \underline{u}(A)$ and $\mathrm{Ad}_G = \mathrm{Ad}_{U(A)}|G$, $\mathrm{ad}_{\underline{g}} = \mathrm{ad}_{\underline{u}(A)}|\underline{g}$. Thus we must compute

$$d(\mathrm{Ad}) : \underline{u}(A) = A \to \underline{\mathrm{aut}}(\underline{u}(A)) \subset gl(A) = \mathrm{End}_k(A).$$

If $y \in A$, $\chi \in A^*$, we define $\chi_y(u) = \chi(uyu^{-1})$, for $u \in U(A)$. We show first that $\chi_y \in k[U(A)]$. Let $m : A \times A \rightarrow A$ be the product, and write

$$\widetilde{m}(\chi) = \sum_i \chi_i' \otimes \chi_i ,$$

where $\chi_i, \chi_i' \in A^*$. This is possible because the product is bilinear. We regard A^* as a subspace of $k[A]$. Then

$$\chi(xy) = \sum_i \chi_i'(x)\chi_i(y) ,$$

for all $x,y \in A$. In particular,

$$\chi(uyu^{-1}) = \sum_{i,j} \chi_i'(u)\chi_{ij}'(y)\chi_{ij}(u^{-1}) ,$$

for $y \in A$, $u \in U(A)$. Therefore

$$\chi_y = \sum_{i,j} \chi_{ij}'(y)\chi_i'\overline{\chi}_{ij} ,$$

where $\overline{\chi}_{ij} \in k[U(A)]$ is defined by $\overline{\chi}_{ij}(u) = \chi_{ij}(u^{-1})$, i.e., $\overline{\chi}_{ij} = \chi_{ij} \circ i$, where $i : U(A) \rightarrow U(A)$ is the inverse. Thus $\chi_y \in k[U(A)]$.

Now the representation of $U(A)$ in A by inner automorphisms induces an operation of $\underline{u}(A)$ on A given by $\chi(X_x y) = x(\chi_y)$, $x,y \in A$, $\chi \in A^*$. In particular, $\chi(X_x 1) = x(\chi) = \chi(x)$. Then

$$\chi(X_x y) = x(\sum \chi_{ij}'(y)\chi_i'\overline{\chi}_{ij}) =$$

$$\sum \chi_{ij}'(y)x(\chi_i')\overline{\chi}_{ij}(1) \quad + \quad \sum \chi_{ij}'(y)\chi_i'(1)x(\overline{\chi}_{ij}) =$$

$$\sum \chi_i'(x)\chi_{ij}'(y)\chi_{ij}(1) \quad - \quad \sum \chi_i'(1)\chi_{ij}'(y)\chi_{ij}(x) =$$

$$= \chi(xy) - \chi(yx) = \chi([x,y]),$$

from which the proposition follows immediately.

COROLLARY 3.35. Let G be an affine group and let N be a closed normal subgroup of G. Then $\underline{n}$ is an ideal in $\underline{g}$.

Proof: Since $a_x N = N$ for all $x \in G$, $da_x \underline{n} \subset \underline{n}$ for all $x \in G$, i.e., $Ad(x)\underline{n} \subset \underline{n}$. Thus $[\underline{g},\underline{n}] \subset \underline{n}$.

COROLLARY 3.36. If G is commutative, then $[\underline{g},\underline{g}] = (0)$.

Proof: Since a_x is the identity, $Ad(x)$ is the identity for all $x \in G$. Therefore $ad(X)(Y) = [X,Y] = 0$ for all $X,Y \in \underline{g}$.

EXERCISE. Show by an example that proposition 3.31 is false if G is not connected.

EXERCISE. If G_1 and G_2 are affine groups and $G = G_1 \times G_2$ show that $\underline{g}$ is canonically isomorphic to $\underline{g}_1 \times \underline{g}_2$ where the product algebra has the bracket $[(X_1,X_2),(Y_1,Y_2)] = ([X_1,Y_1],[X_2,Y_2])$.

CHAPTER IV

REPRESENTATIONS OF LIE ALGEBRAS

IV-1 COMPLETE REDUCIBILITY

Suppose that G is an affine group such that whenever M is a rational G-module and N is a G-submodule of M there exists a G-submodule N' of M with $M = N \oplus N'$. We shall see in chapter V that this property is the key to the invariant theory of G. It implies, for example, that if G acts on an affine algebraic set V over k, then the ring $k[V]^G$ is an affine k-algebra. We have already seen in the proof of theorem 2.26 how this can be the critical step in constructing a quotient of V by G. We have also seen in proposition 3.31 that - at least in characteristic zero - G has the above property if and only if its Lie algebra has the same property, G being connected.

Now the question of whether or not an affine group has the given property may be very difficult to answer if one confines attention to the group itself. However, if one asks which Lie algebras have the corresponding property, then the problem is tractable. In the present chapter, we give a complete solution for Lie algebras over k. The key to this solution lies in making as much use as possible of the 'linear' character of Lie algebras.

DEFINITION 4.1. Let L be a Lie algebra over k. By an L-module we mean a k-vector space M together with a Lie homomorphism $\rho : L \rightarrow \mathrm{End}_k(M)$ where $\mathrm{End}_k(M)$ is regarded as a Lie algebra with bracket $[X,Y] = XY - YX$.

DEFINITION 4.2. An L-module (resp., a rational G-module, G an affine group) is irreducible or simple if, whenever N is an L-submodule (resp., G-submodule) of M, then either $N = M$ or $N = (0)$.

DEFINITION 4.3. An L-module (resp., G-module) M is completely reducible if every L-submodule (resp., G-submodule) N has an L-complement (resp., G-complement), i.e., there exists an L-submodule (resp., G-submodule) N' such that $M = N \oplus N'$.

PROPOSITION 4.4. Let M be a finite dimensional completely reducible L-module. Then M can be written as a direct sum of simple L-submodules. The same holds mutatis mutandis for G-modules.

Proof: Let N be a non-zero simple submodule of M. Such submodules exist, as any minimal submodule is simple. Then if N' is a complement for N, we may assume by induction on the dimension, that N' is a direct sum of simple submodules. Thus M is such a direct sum.

Proposition 3.31 shows that if G is a connected affine group and M is a finite dimensional rational G-module, then M is completely reducible as G-module if and only if M is completely reducible as $\mathfrak{g}$-module - provided that k has characteristic zero! The next proposition allows us to confine our attention to finite dimensional modules.

PROPOSITION 4.5. Let G be a connected affine group. If every finite dimensional rational G-module is completely reducible, then every rational G-module is completely reducible.

Proof: Let M be a rational G-module and let N be a G-submodule. Let N' be a maximal G-submodule of M such that $N \cap N' = (0)$. Such exist by Zorn's lemma. Let $N'' = N + N'$. If $N'' \neq M$, then as M is a union of finite dimensional G-submodules, we can find a simple G-submodule $P \neq (0)$ in M with $P \not\subset N''$. Then $P \cap N'' = (0)$, whence $P + N'' = P \oplus N''$ so that $N + (P + N') = N \oplus (P + N')$, contradicting the maximality of N'.

REMARK. The analogue of proposition 4.5 for Lie algebras is false. If L is a finite dimensional Lie algebra and M is an L-module, it need not be the case that every element of M is contained in a finite dimensional L-submodule. However, as we have already seen, if L is the Lie algebra of an affine group G and the L-module structure on M comes from a rational G-module structure, then M is the union of its finite dimensional L-submodules.

DEFINITION 4.6. If G is an affine group, we say that G is <u>linearly</u> <u>reductive</u> if every rational G-module is completely reducible.

IV-2 THE THEOREMS OF ENGEL AND LIE

<u>N</u>.<u>B</u>. For the remainder of this chapter we shall assume that all Lie algebras and modules are finite dimensional.

If L is a Lie algebra over k and M and N are L-modules, we make $M \otimes_k N$ into an L-module by defining

$$X(m \otimes n) = Xm \otimes n + m \otimes Xn ,$$

for $X \in L$. This is called the <u>diagonal</u> <u>action</u> of L on $M \otimes_k N$.

We make the k-vector space $\mathrm{Hom}_k(M,N)$ of k-linear maps of M into N into an L-module by defining

$$(Xf)(m) = X(fm) - f(Xm) ,$$

for $f \in \mathrm{Hom}_k(M,N)$, $X \in L$.

EXERCISE. Show that the k-vector spaces $M^* \otimes_k N$ and $\mathrm{Hom}_k(M,N)$ are canonically isomorphic. If M and N are L-modules, this gives two ways of defining the action of L on $\mathrm{Hom}_k(M,N)$. Show that they are the same.

We say that an element m of an L-module M is <u>invariant</u> if $Xm = 0$ for all $X \in L$. We denote the set of invariant elements of M by M^L. Clearly, M^L is an L-submodule of M. If $\mathrm{Hom}_L(M,N)$ denotes the set of Lie homomorphisms from the L-module M to the L-module N, then

$$\mathrm{Hom}_L(M,N) = \mathrm{Hom}_k(M,N)^L .$$

The set of bilinear forms on a k-vector space M can be identified with $(M \otimes_k M)^*$. If M is an L-module and B is a bilinear form on M, then B is invariant if and only if

$$(XB)(m \otimes n) = B(Xm \otimes n) + B(m \otimes Xn),$$

for all $m,n \in M$ and all $X \in L$.

If M is an L-module and $\rho : L \to \mathrm{End}_k(M)$ is the defining homomorphism, we set

$$B_\rho(X,Y) = \mathrm{Tr}_M(\rho X \rho Y) ,$$

for $X, Y \in L$. Then B_ρ is a bilinear form on L.

LEMMA 4.7 B_ρ is invariant for the adjoint representation of L.

<u>Proof</u>: $B_\rho([X,Y],Z) + B_\rho(Y,[X,Z]) =$

$$Tr_M(\rho[X,Y]\rho Z) + Tr_M(\rho Y\rho[X,Z]) =$$

$$Tr_M(\rho[X,Y]\rho Z + \rho Y\rho[X,Z]) =$$

$$Tr_M(\rho X\rho Y\rho Z - \rho Y\rho X\rho Z + \rho Y\rho X\rho Z - \rho Y\rho Z\rho X) =$$

$$Tr_M(\rho X\rho Y\rho Z - \rho Y\rho Z\rho X) =$$

$$Tr_M(\rho X(\rho Y\rho Z)) - Tr_M((\rho Y\rho Z)\rho X) = 0,$$

in view of the symmetry of the trace.

DEFINITION 4.8. If L is a Lie algebra, the <u>Killing form</u> of L is the invariant bilinear form

$$B_{ad}(X,Y) = Tr_L(ad(X)ad(Y)).$$

DEFINITION 4.9. Let L be a Lie algebra. Let $C^oL = L$ and $C^nL = [L, C^{n-1}L]$. We say that L is <u>nilpotent</u> if $C^mL = (0)$ for some m. Clearly C^nL is an ideal in L and $[C^iL, C^jL] \subset C^{i+j}L$. It is immediate that L is nilpotent if and only if there exists a chain $L = M_o > M_1 > \cdots > M_n = (0)$ of ideals in L with $[L, M_i] \subset M_{i+1}$. Note that (C^nL) is the shortest chain with this property.

THEOREM 4.10. Let L be a Lie algebra and let M be an L-module such that every element of L acts nilpotently on M. If $M \neq (0)$, then $M^L \neq (0)$.

Proof: We may clearly replace L by its image in $End_k(M)$ and assume that L is a subalgebra of $End_k(M)$. First we show that $ad(X)$ is nilpotent for all $X \in L$. If L_X and R_X are left and right multiplication by X in $End(M)$, then $ad(X)(Y) = L_X(Y) - R_X(Y)$. Since L_X and R_X are nilpotent and commute, $L_X - R_X$ is nilpotent.

Now, by induction on the dimension of L, we may assume the result for subalgebras $L' < L$. Let $\underline{N}(L') = \{X \in L : [X,L'] \subset L'\}$. Then $\underline{N}(L')$ - the normalizer of L' - is a Lie subalgebra of L and L' is an ideal in $\underline{N}(L')$. Since $ad(X)$ is nilpotent for all X, we may assume, by induction, that $(L/L')^{L'} \neq (0)$. But then $\underline{N}(L') > L'$. Repeating the argument, we can find an ideal N in L with $\dim L = 1 + \dim N$. Since N is an ideal in L, M^N is an L-submodule of M, for if $X \in L$, $Y \in N$, and $m \in M^N$, then $YXm - XYm - [X,Y]m = 0$ so $YXm = 0$ and $Xm \in M^N$. Now $M^N \neq (0)$, by induction. If $Y \in L - N$ then since Y acts nilpotently, there is an m M^N with $Ym = 0$, and $m \neq 0$. Since $L = N + kY$, we see that $M^L \neq (0)$.

COROLLARY 4.11. L is a nilpotent Lie algebra if

and only if ad(X) is nilpotent for all $X \in L$.

Proof: If L is nilpotent, it is clear that ad(X) is nilpotent for all $X \in L$. For the converse, apply the theorem with $M = L$ and the adjoint representation.

DEFINITION 4.12. If L is a Lie algebra, set $D^oL = L$ and $D^nL = [D^{n-1}L, D^{n-1}L]$. We say that L is abelian if $D^1L = DL = (0)$, and solvable if $D^mL = (0)$ for some m. Again, as in the case of C^nL, D^nL is an ideal in L and $[D^iL, D^jL] \subset D^{i+j}L$. Also, L is solvable if and only if there is a chain $L = M_o > M_1 > \cdots > M_n = (0)$ of ideals in L with $DM_i \subset M_{i+1}$ for all i.

If L is a Lie algebra and M is an L-module, an element $m \in M$ is called an eigenvector of L if $m \neq 0$ and $Xm \in km$ for all $X \in L$.

Theorem 4.10, known as Engel's theorem, asserts that if L acts nilpotently on M then there exist non-trivial invariants - provided, of course, that $M \neq (0)$. The next theorem, known as Lie's theorem, asserts that if a solvable Lie algebra acts on a module M, then there is an eigenvector - provided that $M \neq (0)$ and the characteristic is zero. The critical step in the proof of Lie's theorem is the following:

LEMMA 4.14. Assume that k has characteristic zero and let L be a Lie algebra over k. If M is an L-module, N is an ideal in L, and m is a non-zero element of M, suppose that there is a map $\chi : L \to k$ such that $Ym = \chi(Y)m$ for all $Y \in N$. Then $\chi([L,N]) = (0)$.

Proof: If $X \in L$, let M_i be the subspace of M spanned by the elements $m, Xm, \ldots, X^{i-1}m$. Choose n minimal such that $M_n = M_{n+1}$. Then $\dim M_n = n$, and $M_{n+p} = M_n$ for $p > 0$, since $XM_n \subset M_n$.

We show by induction on i that for all $Y \in N$,

$$YX^i m \equiv \chi(Y)X^i m \mod M_i ,$$

for all i. If $i = 0$, this is given. If $i > 0$, then

$$\begin{aligned} YX^i m &= YXX^{i-1}m = \\ &XYX^{i-1}m - [X,Y]X^{i-1}m = \\ &X(\chi(Y)X^{i-1}m + m') - [X,Y]X^{i-1}m = \\ &\chi(Y)X^i m + (Xm' - [X,Y]X^{i-1}m) , \end{aligned}$$

for a suitable $m' \in M_{i-1}$. Then the expression in parentheses in the last line is in M_i since $Xm' \in M_i$ and $NM_i \subset M_i$. Thus the matrix of $Y \in N$ with respect to the basis $m, Xm, \ldots, X^{i-1}m$ of M_n is:

$$\begin{pmatrix} \chi(Y) & & & 0 \\ & \chi(Y) & & \\ & & \ddots & \\ * & & & \chi(Y) \end{pmatrix}$$

Thus $Tr_{M_n}(Y) = n\chi(Y)$. Then

$$n\chi([X,Y]) = Tr_{M_n}([X,Y]) = 0 ,$$

so that $\chi([X,Y]) = 0$.

If L is a Lie algebra and M is an L-module, then an eigenvector $m \in M$ of L determines a map $\chi: L \to k$ via $Xm = \chi(X)m$, $X \in L$.

THEOREM 4.15. If k has characteristic zero and L is a solvable Lie algebra over k, then every non-zero L-module M contains an eigenvector of L.

Proof: We use induction on $\dim L$. Assume that $\dim L > 0$ so that $DL < L$. Let N be an ideal in L such that $\dim L = 1 + \dim N$. By induction, there an $m \in M$, $m \neq 0$ such that $Ym = \chi(Y)m$, for all $Y \in N$. Let

$$M' = \{m \in M : Ym = \chi(Y)m \text{ for all } Y \in N\}.$$

By the lemma, if $m \in M'$, $X \in L$, $Y \in N$, then

$$YXm = XYm - [X,Y]m = \chi(Y)Xm - \chi([X,Y])m = \chi(Y)Xm,$$

so that M' is a non-zero L-submodule. If $X \in L - N$, then since k is algebraically closed, $X : M' \to M'$ has an eigenvector m_o. But then m_o is an eigenvector for $N + kX = L$. q.e.d.

IV-3 CARTAN'S CRITERION

In this section we prove a criterion for the solvability of a Lie algebra in characteristic 0. To do this, we need some technical results on endomorphisms which are of interest in themselves and which are not easily found in the literature on linear algebra. The characteristic is 0 throughout.

DEFINITION 4.16. If M is a k-vector space, we say that $X \in \mathrm{End}_k(M)$ is <u>semisimple</u> if its eigenvectors span M. This means that there is a basis of M with respect to which X is represented by a diagonal matrix.

LEMMA 4.17. For any $X \in \mathrm{End}_k(M)$, there exist a semisimple element ${}_sX$ and a nilpotent element ${}_nX$ in $\mathrm{End}_k(M)$ such that $X = {}_sX + {}_nX$, $[{}_sX, {}_nX] = 0$, and ${}_sX$ and ${}_nX$ are uniquely determined by these conditions. Moreover, there exist polynomials $S_X, N_X \in k[T]$ with $S_X(0) = N_X(0) = 0$, such that ${}_sX = S_X(X)$ and ${}_nX = N_X(X)$.

Proof: Write $\det(T - X) = \prod (T - a_i)^{m_i}$ with the a_i distinct elements of k. Let $M_i = \ker(X - a_i)^{m_i}$. Then $M = \bigoplus M_i$ and $XM_i \subset M_i$. Put ${}_sX = \bigoplus a_i 1_{M_i}$, and ${}_nX = X - {}_sX$. Then ${}_sX$ is semisimple and ${}_nX$

is nilpotent since it has no non-zero eigenvalues. Also, $[X, {}_sX] = 0$ since $[X, {}_sX] \mid M_i = 0$ for all i. Thus $[{}_sX, {}_nX] = 0$.

Now if $X = Y + Z$ where Y is semisimple and Z is nilpotent and $[Y,Z] = 0$, then Y has the same eigenvalues on M_i as X, so $Y \mid M_i = {}_sX \mid M_i$, and the uniqueness follows immediately. Finally, let $S_X(T)$ be any polynomial such that $S_X(T) \equiv a_i \bmod (T - a_i)^{m_i}$ and $S_X(T) \equiv 0 \bmod T$, and let $N_X(T) = T - S_X(T)$. Then S_X and N_X clearly have the required properties.

The decomposition of the lemma is called the <u>Jordan decomposition</u> of X. Because ${}_sX$ is a polynomial in X, it follows that if $N \subset N' \subset M$ are subspaces such that $XN' \subset N$, then ${}_sXN' \subset N$. For similar reasons, ${}_nXN' \subset N$. Now let

$$M_{p,q} = T^pM \otimes_k T^qM^* .$$

We make $M_{p,q}$ a module over the Lie algebra $\mathrm{End}_k(M)$ via the diagonal action, so that e.g., $(m, Xn^*) = -(Xm, n^*)$, for $m \in M$, $n^* \in M^*$. In particular, if $p = q = 1$ then $M_{1,1} = M \otimes M^* = \mathrm{End}(M)$, via the map $m \otimes n^* \mapsto (u \mapsto m(u,n^*))$.

LEMMA 4.18. If $X \in \mathrm{End}_k(M)$, then $\mathrm{ad}(X) = X \otimes 1 - 1 \otimes X^*$.

<u>Proof</u>: If $m \in M$, $n^* \in M^*$, $u \in M$, then

$$\mathrm{ad}(X)(m \otimes n^*)u =$$

$$X(m \otimes n^*)u - (m \otimes n^*)Xu =$$

$$(u,n^*)Xm - (Xu,n^*)m =$$

$$(u,n^*)Xm - (u,X^*n^*)m =$$

$$(Xm \otimes n^*)u - (m \otimes X^*n^*)u .$$

Letting $X_{p,q}$ denote the endomorphism of $M_{p,q}$ induced by $X \in \mathrm{End}(M)$ via the diagonal action, we see, by the lemma, that $X_{1,1} = \mathrm{ad}(X)$. Note that $X_{p,q}$ is <u>not</u> $T^p(X) \otimes T^q(X^*)$!

LEMMA 4.19. $({}_sX)_{p,q} + ({}_nX)_{p,q}$ is the Jordan decomposition of $X_{p,q}$.

<u>Proof</u>: Since the map $X \mapsto X_{p,q}$ is linear, the stated equality holds. To prove that this is the Jordan decomposition of $X_{p,q}$ it suffices to show that $({}_sX)_{p,q}$ is semisimple, $({}_nX)_{p,q}$ is nilpotent, and these two endomorphisms of $M_{p,q}$ commute.

If (e_i) is an eigenbasis for ${}_sX$, then (e_i^*) is an eigenbasis for ${}_sX^*$. It then follows that $(e_{i_1} \otimes \cdots \otimes e_{i_p} \otimes e_{j_1}^* \otimes \cdots \otimes e_{j_q}^*)$ is an eigenbasis for $({}_sX)_{p,q}$. Also, $({}_nX)_{p,q}$ is a sum of endomorphisms of the form $1 \otimes \cdots \otimes {}_nX \otimes \cdots \otimes 1$, $1 \otimes \cdots \otimes {}_nX^* \otimes \cdots \otimes 1$ which are commuting nilpotent endomorphisms, so that $({}_nX)_{p,q}$ is nilpotent. Finally, $[({}_sX)_{p,q}, ({}_nX)_{p,q}] = [{}_sX, {}_nX]_{p,q} = 0.$

If $\mathbf{Q}$ denotes the field of rational numbers, φ is an element of $\mathrm{Hom}_{\mathbf{Q}}(k,k)$, and X is a semisimple endomorphism of M, with eigendecomposition $M = \bigoplus M_i$, $X|M_i = a_i 1_{M_i}$, we define $\varphi_i(X) = \varphi(a_i)1_{M_i}$ and $\varphi(X)$ as the direct sum of the $\varphi_i(X)$. Since there are only finitely many a_i, we can find a polynomial P with $P(0) = 0$ and $\varphi(X) = P(X)$.

LEMMA 4.20. If X is a semisimple element of $\mathrm{End}_k(M)$, then $\varphi(X)_{p,q} = \varphi(X_{p,q})$ for all $\varphi \in \mathrm{Hom}_{\mathbf{Q}}(k,k)$.

<u>Proof</u>: On $M_{i_1} \otimes \cdots \otimes M_{i_p} \otimes M^*_{j_1} \otimes \cdots \otimes M^*_{j_q}$, $X_{p,q}$ is the scalar $a_{i_1} + \cdots + a_{i_p} - a_{j_1} - \cdots - a_{j_q}$ and $\varphi(X_{p,q})$ is the scalar $\varphi(a_{i_1}) + \cdots + \varphi(a_{i_p}) - \varphi(a_{j_1}) - \cdots - \varphi(a_{j_q})$.

Since, for any $X \in \mathrm{End}(M)$, $\varphi({}_sX)_{p,q}$ can be expressed as a polynomial in $X_{p,q}$, it follows that if $N \subset N' \subset M_{p,q}$ are subspaces such that $X_{p,q}N' \subset N$, then $\varphi({}_sX)_{p,q}N' \subset N$. The fact we will need for the proof of Cartan's criterion is the following:

LEMMA 4.21. If $X \in \mathrm{End}_k(M)$ and $\mathrm{Tr}_M(X\varphi({}_sX)) = 0$ for all $\varphi \in \mathrm{Hom}_{\mathbf{Q}}(k,k)$, then ${}_sX = 0$.

<u>Proof</u>: Using the eigendecomposition of X given above, we have $Tr_M(X\varphi({}_sX)) = \sum m_i a_i \varphi(a_i) = 0$, for all φ. If φ takes k into $\mathbf{Q}$, apply φ again to get $\sum m_i \varphi(a_i)^2 = 0$, so that $\varphi(a_i) = 0$ for all $\varphi \in Hom_{\mathbf{Q}}(k,\mathbf{Q})$ and so $a_i = 0$ for all i. Thus ${}_sX = 0$.

THEOREM 4.22. If L is a Lie subalgebra of $End_k(M)$ and k has characteristic zero, then L is solvable if and only if $Tr_M(XY) = 0$ for all $X \in L$ and all $Y \in DL$.

<u>Proof</u>: If L is solvable, then theorem 4.15 implies that there is a chain $M = M_o > M_1 > \ldots > M_n = (0)$ of L-submodules of M with $\dim M_i = 1 + \dim M_{i+1}$. Then

$$Tr_M(XY) = \sum_{i=o}^{n-1} Tr_{M_i/M_{i+1}}(XY) = 0 ,$$

since $Y \in DL$ must annihilate any 1-dimensional L-module.

Conversely, by theorem 4.10, it suffices to show that any $Y \in DL$ is nilpotent. If we write $Y = {}_sY + {}_nY$, it then suffices to show that $Tr_M(Y\varphi({}_sY)) = 0$ for all $\varphi \in Hom_{\mathbf{Q}}(k,k)$. Since $Y \in DL$, we can write $Y = \sum_{i,j} c_{ij}[X_i,X_j]$, $c_{ij} \in k$, X_i, X_j L. Then

$$Tr_M(Y\varphi({}_sY)) = \sum_{i,j} c_{ij} Tr_M([X_i,X_j]\varphi({}_sY)) =$$

$$\sum_{i,j} c_{ij} \mathrm{Tr}_M(X_j[\varphi(_sY), X_i])$$

so it suffices to prove that $[\varphi(_sY), X_i] \in DL$. As $Y_{1,1}(X) = YX - XY = [Y,X]$, it follows that $Y_{1,1}L \subset DL$ and so $\varphi(_sY)_{1,1}L \subset DL$ as required.

IV-4 SEMISIMPLE LIE ALGEBRAS

In this section we define semisimplicity for Lie algebras and show that the Lie algebras of the classical groups in characteristic zero are semisimple. This is done by showing that semisimplicity is equivalent to non-degeneracy of the Killing form in characteristic zero and then explicitly computing the Killing forms of $\underline{sl}_n$, $\underline{o}_n$, and $\underline{sp}_n$. All this breaks down completely in positive characteristics, as we shall see later.

LEMMA 4.23. Let L be a Lie algebra and let N, N' be solvable ideals in L. Then $N + N'$ is a solvable ideal.

Proof: That $N + N'$ is an ideal is obvious. On the other hand, we have the isomorphism $N + N'/N \approx N'/N \cap N'$ and the latter is a solvable ideal in $L/N \cap N'$. Since $N \cap N'$ is solvable, the lemma follows.

DEFINITION 4.24. If L is a Lie algebra, we define

the radical of L to be the largest solvable ideal in L. We denote this ideal by $\underline{r}(L)$. That $\underline{r}(L)$ exists is an immediate consequence of lemma 4.23. We say that L is semisimple if $\underline{r}(L) = (0)$.

THEOREM 4.25. If k has characteristic zero, then the Lie algebra L is semisimple if and only if the Killing form of L is non-degenerate.

Proof: Let $N = \{X \in L : Tr_L(ad(X)ad(Y)) = 0$ for all $Y \in L\}$. Since the Killing form is invariant, N is an ideal in L. By theorem 4.22, ad(N) is a solvable Lie subalgebra of End(L). As ad(N) = N/(center of N), it follows that N is a solvable ideal in L. Hence, if L is semisimple, N = (0).

Conversely, if the Killing form is non-degenerate, we show that any abelian ideal of L lies in N and hence is (0). From this it will follow that $\underline{r}(L) = (0)$. If A is an abelian ideal of L, and $X \in A$, $Y \in L$, let $H = ad(X)ad(Y)$. Then $HL \subset A$, $HA = (0)$, so that $H^2L = (0)$ and thus $Tr_L H = 0$. Thus $A \subset N$ as required.

EXERCISE. Show that if M and N are k-vector spaces and $X \in End_k(M)$, $Y \in End_k(N)$, then $Tr_{M \otimes_k N}(X \otimes Y) = Tr_M(X) Tr_N(Y)$.

Recall that $\underline{sl}_n$ can be identified with the ideal of matrices of trace zero in $\underline{gl}_n$. To compute the Killing form of $\underline{sl}_n$, we remind the reader that one can pass from quadratic forms Q on a vector space M to symmetric bilinear forms B on M by the familiar polarization process, viz., if B is symmetric bilinear, and $Q(x) = B(x,x)$, then $B(x,y) = \frac{1}{2}(Q(x + y) - Q(x) - Q(y))$.

PROPOSITION 4.26. The Killing form of $\underline{sl}_n$ is $2n \cdot Tr_{\underline{A}^n}(XY)$, X,Y $\underline{sl}_n$.

Proof: Setting $\underline{A}^n = M$, we have:

$$Tr_{M\otimes M^*}(ad(X)^2) =$$

$$Tr_{M\otimes M^*}((X\otimes 1 - 1\otimes X^*)^2) =$$

$$Tr_{M\otimes M^*}(X^2\otimes 1 + 1\otimes X^{*2} - 2X\otimes X^*) =$$

$$2n\cdot Tr_M(X^2) - 2(Tr_M(X))^2.$$

Since X has trace 0, the proposition follows by polarization.

In order to compute the Killing forms of $\underline{o}_n$ and $\underline{sp}_n$, we need a few preliminaries. First note that if B is a non-degenerate bilinear form on the vector space M, then we can use B to identify $M\otimes M^* = M_{1,1}$ with $M\otimes M = M_{2,0}$. Next, we define a symmetry operator $S \in End(M\otimes M)$ by $S(m\otimes n) = n\otimes m$. Then $S^2 = 1$ and $\frac{1}{2}((1 + S) + (1 - S)) = 1$. Also $(1 + S)(1 - S) = 0$. This expresses the familiar fact that any matrix can be uniquely expressed as the sum of a symmetric matrix and a skew-symmetric matrix. $\frac{1}{2}(1 + S)$ is the projection on the space of symmetric operators and $\frac{1}{2}(1 - S)$ is the projection on the space of skew-symmetric operators.

Now if $X \in \mathrm{End}(M)$, we define $\overline{X}$ by $B(\overline{X}m,n) = B(m,Xn)$, $m,n \in M$. If $X = x \otimes y \in \mathrm{End}(M) = M_{2,0}$ (according to our identifications) then

$$B(Xm,n) = B((x \otimes y)m,n) = B(B(m,y)x,n) = B(m,y)B(x,n),$$

$$B(m,Xn) = B(m,(x \otimes y)n) = B(m,B(n,x)y) = B(m,y)B(n,x).$$

It follows from this that if B is symmetric, then $\overline{X} = SX$ and if B is skew-symmetric, then $\overline{X} = -SX$. On the other hand, the condition that X belong to the appropriate algebra - $\underline{o}_n$ in the symmetric case and $\underline{sp}_n$ in the skew case - is always given by $\overline{X} = -X$, since $B(Xm,n) + B(m,Xn) = 0$ is the condition that B be invariant for X.

LEMMA 4.27. If $X,Y \in \mathrm{End}_k(M)$, then $\mathrm{Tr}_{M \otimes M}(S(X \otimes Y)) = \mathrm{Tr}_M(XY)$.

<u>Proof</u>: This is most easily done using bases. Let $e_1,\ldots,e_n$ be a basis of M. Then we need only check the formula for $X = e_j \otimes e_i$, $Y = e_q \otimes e_p$. Then

$$\mathrm{Tr}_M(XY) = \mathrm{Tr}_M((e_j \otimes e_i)(e_q \otimes e_p)) =$$

$$\delta_{iq}\mathrm{Tr}_M(e_j \otimes e_p) = \delta_{iq}\,\delta_{pj}\ .$$

Now we have:

$$S(X \otimes Y)(m \otimes n) = S(Xm \otimes Yn) =$$

$$S(B(m,e_i)e_j \otimes B(n,e_p)e_q) =$$

$$B(m,e_i)e_q \otimes B(n,e_p)e_j =$$

$$((e_q \otimes e_i)m) \otimes ((e_j \otimes e_p)n).$$

Thus

$$Tr_{M \otimes M}(S(X \otimes Y)) =$$

$$Tr_{M \otimes M}((e_q \otimes e_i) \otimes (e_j \otimes e_p)) =$$

$$\delta_{iq}\, \delta_{pj}\, .$$

Next we note that the condition that X belong to $\underline{o}_n$ is $SX = -X$ (since in this case $\bar{X} = SX$), and the condition that X belong to $\underline{sp}_n$ is $SX = X$ (since in this case $\bar{X} = -SX$).

Finally, we remark that if M is any k-vector space, M' a subspace, P a projection of M on M', and T an operator on M leaving M' invariant, then $Tr_{M'}(T) = Tr_M(PT)$.

PROPOSITION 4.28. The Killing form of $\underline{o}_n$ is

$$\tfrac{1}{2}(n - 2)\cdot Tr_{\underline{A}^n}(XY) \qquad X,Y \in \underline{o}_n.$$

The Killing form of $\underline{sp}_n$ is

$$(n + 1)\cdot Tr_{\underline{A}^{2n}}(XY) \qquad X,Y \in \underline{sp}_n.$$

Proof: We compute the two forms together, so that

M is either $\underline{A}^n$ or $\underline{A}^{2n}$ and $d = \dim M$. L denotes either $\underline{o}_n$ or $\underline{sp}_n$ and $X = \frac{1}{2}(1 \pm S)X$.
Then

$$\mathrm{Tr}_L(\mathrm{ad}(X)^2) =$$
$$\mathrm{Tr}_{M\otimes M}(\tfrac{1}{2}(1 \pm S)\mathrm{ad}(X)^2) =$$
$$\tfrac{1}{2}\,\mathrm{Tr}_{M\otimes M}((1 \pm S)(X\otimes 1 - 1\otimes \overline{X})^2) =$$
$$\tfrac{1}{2}\,\mathrm{Tr}_{M\otimes M}((1 \pm S)(X\otimes 1 + 1\otimes X)^2) =$$
$$\tfrac{1}{2}\,\mathrm{Tr}_{M\otimes M}((1 \pm S)(X^2\otimes 1 + 1\otimes X^2 + 2X\otimes X)) =$$
$$d\cdot\mathrm{Tr}_M(X^2) + \mathrm{Tr}_M(X)^2$$
$$\pm \tfrac{1}{2}(\mathrm{Tr}_{M\otimes M}(S(X^2\otimes 1 + 1\otimes X^2 + 2X\otimes X))) =$$
$$d\cdot\mathrm{Tr}_M(X^2) + \mathrm{Tr}_M(X)^2 \pm 2\mathrm{Tr}_M(X^2) =$$
$$(d \pm 2)\mathrm{Tr}_M(X^2) + \mathrm{Tr}_M(X)^2 =$$
$$(d \pm 2)\mathrm{Tr}_M(X^2)\ .$$

The last equality holds because $X = -\overline{X}$ implies $\mathrm{Tr}_M(X) = 0$. The proposition then follows by polarization.

EXERCISE. Show that $\underline{o}_n$ can be identified with the set of skew-symmetric matrices in $\underline{gl}_n$.

EXERCISE. Show that $\underline{A}^n$ carries a non-degenerate skew 2-form if and only if n is even. Obtain a canonical expression for this form. Show that if $X \in \mathrm{End}_k(\underline{A}^n)$, $n = 2m$, is expressed as a matrix:

$$X = \begin{pmatrix} A & B \\ C & D \end{pmatrix}$$

with respect to the canonical basis, then $X \in \underline{sp}_n$ if and only if $D = -{}^tA$ and B and C are symmetric.

THEOREM 4.29. The Lie algebras

$$\underline{sl}_n \qquad (n \geqslant 2)$$

$$\underline{o}_n \qquad (n \geqslant 3)$$

$$\underline{sp}_n \qquad (n \geqslant 1)$$

are semisimple.

Proof: First we show that $\underline{sl}_n$ is semisimple. We must have $n \geqslant 2$, since $\underline{sl}_1$ is trivial. If we have $Tr(XY) = 0$ for all X, then evidently $Y = 0$. Furthermore, if $Tr(ZX) = 0$ for all X of trace 0, then Z is a scalar matrix. To see this second assertion, let $a = (1/n)Tr(Z)$. Then $Tr((Z - a1)X) = 0$ whenever X has trace 0. Also, $Tr((Z - a1)1) = 0$ so that $Tr((Z - a1)X) = 0$ for all X. Thus $Z - a1 = 0$. But then $Tr(Z) = 0$ implies $Z = 0$. Therefore the Killing form of $\underline{sl}_n$ is non-degenerate.

In the case of $\underline{o}_n$ or $\underline{sp}_n$, if $Tr(ZX) = 0$ for all $X \in L$, take $X = Y - \overline{Y}$. Then

$$0 = Tr(ZY) - Tr(Z\overline{Y}) = Tr(ZY) - Tr(\overline{Z}Y) =$$

$$\mathrm{Tr}((Z - \bar{Z})Y) = 0.$$

As Y is arbitrary, we have $Z - \bar{Z} = 0$, but since $Z \in L$, we have $Z + \bar{Z} = 0$. Therefore $Z = 0$. Thus $\underline{o}_n$ and $\underline{sp}_n$ are semisimple.

In connection with this, one should note that $\underline{sp}_1 = \underline{sl}_2$, that $\underline{sl}_1$ and $\underline{o}_1$ are trivial, and that $\underline{o}_2$ is abelian.

If k is the field of complex numbers, one can show that - aside from the infinite families $\underline{sl}_n$ $(n \geq 2)$, $\underline{o}_n$ $(n \geq 3)$, and $\underline{sp}_n$ $(n \geq 1)$ - there are only five semisimple Lie algebras: G_2, F_4, E_6, E_7, E_8. All these algebras come from affine groups. For these and related matters, see: J.-P. Serre, Les Algebres de Lie Semi-simples Complexes, (Benjamin).

IV-5 WEYL'S THEOREM

From the viewpoint of invariant theory, this is the key result on semisimple Lie algebras in characteristic zero. We will see in chapter V that it is the crux of the construction of quotients of affine algebraic sets by semisimple groups.

If L is a Lie algebra over k, let $T(L)$ be the tensor algebra of L over k and let I_L be the two-sided ideal in $T(L)$ generated by all elements of the form $[X,Y] - X \otimes Y + Y \otimes X$, $X, Y \in L$.

Let $U(L) = T(L)/I_L$. $U(L)$ is called the <u>universal associative algebra</u> of L or the <u>enveloping algebra</u> of L. It is clear from the universal mapping property of the tensor algebra that $U(L)$ is itself characterized by the following universal mapping property:

> If $\psi : L \to A$ is a k-linear mapping of L into an associative k-algebra A such
that that $\psi[X,Y] = \psi(X)\,\psi(Y) - \psi(Y)\,\psi(X)$, for all $X, Y \in L$, then there is a unique (associative) k-algebra homomorphism, $\eta : U(L) \to A$ such that $\psi = \eta \circ \varphi$, where φ is the canonical map $L = T^1L \to U(L)$.

In other words, to give a module over the Lie algebra L is the same thing as to give a module over the associative algebra $U(L)$.

LEMMA 4.30. Let A be an algebra - not necessarily associative - and let M be a simple A-module. If $f : M \to M$ is an A-endomorphism, then either f is surjective or $f = 0$.

<u>Proof</u>: fM is an A-submodule of M so $fM = M$ or $fM = (0)$.

PROPOSITION 4.31. Let L be a semisimple Lie algebra, N an ideal of L, and let N' be the ortho-

gonal space of N with respect to the Killing form, i.e., $N' = \{Y \in L : B_{ad}(X,Y) = 0$ for all $X \in N\}$. Then N' is an ideal of L and $L = N \oplus N'$.

N.B. The convention that k has characteristic 0 is still in force.

Proof: Since the Killing form is invariant, N' is an ideal. By theorem 4.22, $N \cap N'$ is a solvable ideal in L, so that $N \cap N' = (0)$. The remainder of the proof we leave as an exercise, viz.

EXERCISE. Let B be a non-degenerate bilinear form on the vector space M and let N be a subspace of M. If $N' = \{m \in M : B(n,m) = 0$ for all $n \in N\}$, then $\dim N' = \dim M - \dim N$.

DEFINITION 4.32. A Lie algebra L is simple (in any characteristic) if L is non-abelian and has no proper ideals.

COROLLARY 4.33. A semisimple Lie algebra is a direct sum of simple ideals.

COROLLARY 4.34. If L is a semisimple Lie algebra and N is an ideal of L, then L/N is semisimple.

Proof: If N' is the orthogonal space of N with respect to the Killing form, then L/N is isomorphic to N'. N' is semisimple because a non-zero abelian ideal in N' would be an ideal in L as $[N,N'] = (0)$.

THEOREM 4.35. Let L be a semisimple Lie algebra over the algebraically closed field k of characteristic zero. Then every L-module is completely reducible.

Proof: We remind the reader of our convention that all modules are finite dimensional. We proceed in a series of reductions. Given an exact sequence of L-modules and L-homomorphisms

$$(1) \qquad 0 \to M \to N \xrightarrow{\alpha} P \to 0 ,$$

we seek a complementary submodule for M in N, i.e. an L-submodule of N which is mapped bijectively to P by α. To do this, let W be the k-subspace of $\mathrm{Hom}_k(N,M)$ consisting of linear maps whose restriction to M is a scalar mapping, and let V be the subspace of W consisting of maps whose restriction to M is 0. V and W are L-submodules of $\mathrm{Hom}_k(N,M)$. If either M or P is trivial, there is nothing to prove, so we may assume that we have an exact sequence of L-modules

$$(2) \qquad 0 \to V \to W \to k \to 0 .$$

If we can solve the problem for (2) then, as L must act trivially on any 1-dimensional L-module, we can find an L-invariant element $\psi \in W$ mapping onto $1 \in k$, i.e., an L-homomorphism of N onto M whose restriction to M is 1. Then $\ker \psi$ solves the problem for (1)

To solve the problem for (2), we first reduce to the case where V is simple. If V' is a proper submodule of V, we have an exact sequence

$$0 \to V/V' \to W/V' \to k \to 0 .$$

By induction on the dimension, we may assume that there is a 1-dimensional L-submodule V_o/V' in W/V' mapping onto k. This yields an exact sequence

$$0 \to V' \to V_o \to k \to 0 ,$$

and, again by induction, we can find a 1-dimensional L-submodule V_1 in V_o mapping onto k. Then V_1 is a submodule of W with the required properties.

Next we reduce to the case where $\rho : L \to \mathrm{End}(V)$ is injective. In any case, if $L' = \ker \rho$, then L' is semisimple, whence by corollary 4.32, $DL' = L'$. But if $X \in L'$, then $XW \subset V$ and $XV = (0)$ so that $(DL')W = (0)$, i.e., $L'W = (0)$. Thus L/L' on W and is semisimple. Therefore we may assume that V is simple and L acts faithfully on V.

Now we come to the heart of the proof! By theorem 4.22, the ideal of all $X \in L$ such that $B (X,Y) = 0$ for all $Y \in L$ is zero, i.e., B_ρ is non-degenerate. This means that we can find dual bases (X_i) and (Y_j) for L with respect to B, i.e., $B(X_i, Y_j) = \delta_{ij}$. Let b be the element $\sum_i X_i Y_i$ of $U(L)$. We define an L-isomorphism of $L \otimes_k L$ with $\mathrm{Hom}_k(L,L)$ by sending $X \otimes Y$ to the homomorphism η given by $\eta(Z) = B_\rho(Z,Y)X$. Then $\sum_i X_i \otimes Y_i$ maps to the identity 1_L. Because 1_L lies in $\mathrm{Hom}_k(L,L)^L$, it follows that $\sum_i X_i \otimes Y_i \in (L \otimes_k L)^L$ and hence that b is in the center of $U(L)$.

By the universal mapping property of $U(L)$, b defines an L-endomorphism of V and

$$\mathrm{Tr}_V(b) = \mathrm{Tr}_V(\sum_i \rho X_i \rho Y_i) =$$

$$\sum \mathrm{Tr}_V(\rho X_i \rho Y_i) = \sum B_\rho(X_i, Y_i) = \dim L.$$

Since V is simple, and $\mathrm{Tr}_V(b) \neq 0$, it follows from lemma 4.30 that b defines an automorphism of V. Finally, since L acts trivially on k, we have $bW \subset V$. Since $bV = V$, $\ker b$ is the required L-complement to V in W. q.e.d.

DEFINITION 4.36. If k has characteristic zero, a connected affine group G is said to be <u>semisimple</u> if $\underline{g}$ is semisimple. We say that G is <u>solvable</u> if $\underline{g}$ is solvable. This is a provosional definition. We will show in chapter V that it agrees -

in characteristic zero - with the group-theoretical notions of semisimplicity and solvability.

COROLLARY 4.37. A semisimple affine group over an algebraically closed field of characteristic zero is linearly reductive.

What we have established is this. If k has characteristic zero, the groups

$$SL_n \quad (n \geqslant 2),$$
$$O_n \quad (n \geqslant 3),$$
$$Sp_n \quad (n \geqslant 1),$$

are linearly reductive. Note that the groups SL_1 and O_1 are finite - $SL_1 = (1)$ and $O_1 = (\pm 1)$.

It is easy to show that any finite group is linearly reductive in characteristic zero. To see this, let G be a finite group of order g, and let $\rho : G \to GL(M)$ be a representation. If N is a G-submodule of M, let P be a linear projection of M onto N, and let

$$P_o = \frac{1}{g} \sum_{x \in G} \rho(x) P \rho(x^{-1}) .$$

EXERCISE. Show that P_o is a G-linear projection of M onto N and that $\ker P_o$ is a G-complement for N in M. Show that the same argument works in characteristic p, provided g is prime to p.

The only case left is O_2. This group is linearly reductive in any characteristic but 2. It has a faithful representation on $\underline{A}^2$ as the subgroup of GL_2 leaving the form $X^2 + Y^2$ invariant. But

$$X^2 + Y^2 = (X + iY)(X - iY) = UV .$$

This means that, for a suitable basis of $\underline{A}^n$, O_2 is represented by matrices

$$\begin{pmatrix} a & 0 \\ 0 & a^{-1} \end{pmatrix}$$

i.e., is isomorphic to G_m.

EXERCISE. Without looking at proposition 5.23, show that the group G_m is linearly reductive in any characteristic.

REMARK. In the classical theory of form invariants, the group $PGL_n = GL_{n+1}/G_m$ where G_m is the subgroup of scalar matrices, played the central role. Note that PGL_n can also be represented as SL_{n+1}/C, where C is a cyclic group of order $n + 1$, identifiable as the group of scalar matrices $\varpi 1$, where ϖ is an $(n + 1)$-st root of unity. Theorem 3.29 shows that $\underline{pgl}_n = \underline{sl}_{n+1}$ so that PGL_n is a linearly reductive group. This also follows directly from the fact that PGL_n is a quotient of SL_{n+1}, so that a rational PGL_n-module M is a rational SL_{n+1}-module, and a PGL_n-submodule $N \subset M$ is an SL_{n+1}

submodule and conversely.

IV-6 REDUCTIVE LIE ALGEBRAS

In this section, we introduce the notion of a reductive Lie algebra. We use this to study which modules over a given Lie algebra are completely reducible.

DEFINITION 4.38. A Lie algebra L is said to be a <u>reductive algebra</u> if L is a completely reducible L-module, i.e., the adjoint representation is completely reducible.

PROPOSITION 4.39. If k has characteristic zero and L is a Lie algebra over k, then the following are equivalent.

i) L is a reductive algebra.

ii) $[L,L]$ is a semisimple Lie algebra.

iii) $L = Z \times S$ where Z is abelian and S is semisimple.

iv) L admits a faithful completely reducible module.

v) $\underline{r}(L)$ is the center of L.

<u>Proof</u>: i) implies ii). By i), L is a direct sum of simple ideals N_i. Then $[N_i,N_i]$ is either N_i

or (0). Thus

$$[L,L] = \bigoplus_{i,j} [N_i,N_j] = \bigoplus_i N_i .$$

The only non-zero summands in the last sum are those ideals which are simple Lie algebras. Thus [L,L] is semisimple.

ii) implies iii). By semisimplicity of [L,L], we see that L = [L,L] x Z, where Z is an ideal of L. But then Z is isomorphic to L/[L,L], so Z is abelian.

iii) implies iv). Since any abelian Lie algebra is a direct sum of 1-dimensional ideals, and any 1-dimensional Lie algebra is isomorphic to k, it follows that an abelian algebra always admits a faithful completely reducible module. Thus if M is a faithful completely reducible Z-module, we may take M x [L,L] as our faithful completely reducible L-module.

iv) implies v). Since $\underline{r}(L)$ is solvable, lemma 4.14 implies that $[L,\underline{r}(L)]$ annihilates every eigenvector of L, and, by repeated application, that $[L,\underline{r}(L)]$ acts nilpotently on every L-module. Thus $[L,\underline{r}(L)]M = (0)$ if M is a simple L-module, and hence also if M is completely reducible. Therefore if there exists a faithful completely reducible L-module, then $[L,\underline{r}(L)] = (0)$, whence $\underline{r}(L)$ is the center of L.

v) implies i). Note that L as L-module is

the same as L as $L/\underline{r}(L)$-module when the radical is the center. But $L/\underline{r}(L)$ is a semisimple algebra.

THEOREM 4.40. Let L be a Lie algebra and M an L-module. If k has characteristic zero, then the following are equivalent.

i) M is a completely reducible L-module.

ii) If $\rho: L \to \mathrm{End}_k(M)$ is the structure homomorphism and $\overline{L} = L/\ker\rho$, then $\overline{L}$ is a reductive algebra, and its center, considered as a subalgebra of $\mathrm{End}_k(M)$, consists of semisimple endomorphisms.

iii) M is a completely reducible $\underline{r}(L)$-module.

Proof: To prove i) and ii) equivalent, we may replace L by $\overline{L}$ and assume that L is a subalgebra of End(M). It is a well-known theorem in linear algebra that a commutative set of diagonalizable matrices can be simultaneously diagonalized. If ii) holds, then we may write M as a direct sum of eigenspaces for the center. By lemma 4.14, each of these eigenspaces is an L-submodule. Since $L = Z \times S$, where Z is the center of L and S is semisimple, each eigenspace is completely reducible. Thus ii) implies i). Conversely, by theorem 4.15, there is an eigenvector $m \in M$ for $\underline{r}(L)$. There is then a linear mapping $\chi : \underline{r}(L) \to k$ such that $Xm = \chi(X)m$ for all $X \in \underline{r}(L)$. Let

$$M_\chi = \{m \in M : Xm = \chi(X)m \text{ for all } X \in \underline{r}(L)\}.$$

By lemma 4.14, M_χ is an L-submodule of M. Since M is completely reducible, we can find linear forms χ_i on $\underline{r}(L)$ such that $M = \bigoplus_i M_{\chi_i}$. Thus $\underline{r}(L)$ acts diagonally on M and commutes with the action of L. Therefore $\underline{r}(L)$ is the center of L and L is reductive, by proposition 4.39.

To see that ii) implies iii), note that the image of $\underline{r}(L)$ in $\bar{L}$ is solvable, hence central, and therefore $\underline{r}(L)$ acts diagonally on M. For the converse, note that if M is completely reducible as $\underline{r}(L)$-module, theorem 4.15 implies that $\underline{r}(L)$ acts diagonally on M. Thus $\underline{r}(L)$ is mapped into the center of $\bar{L}$. Since $L/\underline{r}(L)$ is semisimple, $\underline{r}(L)$ must be mapped onto the center of $\bar{L}$. Then we can apply v) of proposition 4.39.

COROLLARY 4.41. In characteristic zero, GL_n is a linearly reductive group.

Proof: Since the radical of $\underline{gl}_n$ is the Lie algebra of G_m, it suffices to show that G_m is a linearly reductive group. For this, see proposition 5.23

REMARK. Note that we have not proved - nor is it

true - that every finite dimensional $\underline{gl}_n$-module is completely reducible. Since $\underline{gl}_n = k \times \underline{sl}_n$, it suffices to find a k-module which is not completely reducible. But the one coming from the well-known representation

$$\begin{pmatrix} 1 & a \\ 0 & 1 \end{pmatrix}$$

of G_a will suffice.

IV-7 COUNTEREXAMPLES IN CHARACTERISTIC p.

Almost everything that we have proved in characteristic zero about Lie algebras is totally false in characteristic $p > 0$. Not only the results, but the methods as well, break down completely. We now illustrate this by giving counterexamples to the three cornerstones of the theory - Lie's theorem (4.15), Cartan's criterion (4.22), and Weyl's theorem (4.35).

1 - Lie's theorem.

The simplest example is given by $\underline{sl}_2$ in characteristic 2. In this case, $\underline{sl}_2$ is actually nilpotent, but it has no eigenvector in $\underline{A}^2$. Note that this is not a counterexample to Engel's theorem (4.10), since $\underline{sl}_2$ does not act nilpotently on $\underline{A}^2$.

EXERCISE. Construct a counterexample to Lie's theorem in each positive characteristic.

2 - Cartan's criterion.

Since $\underline{sl}_n$ consists of the matrices in $\underline{gl}_n$ with trace 0, it follows that $\underline{sl}_n$ has a linear basis

$$E_{ii} - E_{nn}, \qquad 1 \leqslant i \leqslant n-1,$$
$$E_{ij}, \qquad i \neq j,$$

where E_{ij} denotes the matrix with 1 as (i,j)-th entry and zeroes elsewhere. The relations are

$$[E_{jn}, E_{nj}] = E_{jj} - E_{nn},$$
$$[E_{jj} - E_{nn}, E_{jn}] = 2E_{jn},$$
$$[E_{jj} - E_{nn}, E_{nj}] = -2E_{nj},$$
$$[E_{in}, E_{nj}] = E_{ij}, \quad i \neq j, \quad i \neq n \neq j.$$

All other brackets are zero. It follows that if k does not have characteristic 2, then $D\underline{sl}_n = \underline{sl}_n$. Thus $\underline{sl}_n$ is not solvable. However, if p divides n then the Killing form of $\underline{sl}_n$ is identically zero.

3 - Weyl's theorem.

Here the breakdown is total. We prove a theorem of Iwasawa which implies that Weyl's theorem is false for <u>every</u> non-trivial Lie algebra in characteristic

$p > 0$.

Let k have characteristic $p > 0$. We say that $f(T) \in k[T]$ is a p-polynomial if $f(T) = \sum a_i T^{p^i}$. Now let L be a Lie algebra over k and let $U(L)$ be its enveloping algebra. If $X, Y \in L$, we set $h_X(Y) = [X,Y] = XY - YX$ in $U(L)$. Then

$$h_X^n(Y) = h_X(h_X \cdots (h_X(Y))) = \sum_{i=0}^{n} (-1)^i \binom{n}{i} X^{n-i} Y X^i$$

Thus $h_X^p(Y) = X^p Y - YX^p = [X^p, Y]$ in $U(L)$. Also, $h_X^{p^n}(Y) = [X^{p^n}, Y]$ in $U(L)$. If f is a p-polynomial such that $f(h_X)(Y) = 0$, then $[f(X), Y] = 0$. Thus if $f(h_X)L = (0)$, then $f(X)$ is in the center of $U(L)$.

THEOREM 4.42. If k has characteristic $p > 0$, and L is a Lie algebra over k, then there is an ideal I in $U(L)$, generated by a finite number of central elements of $U(L)$, such that $U(L)/I$ is a finite dimensional faithful L-module.

<u>Proof</u>: Let $X_1, \ldots, X_n$ be a basis of L over k. Let $m_i(T)$ be the monic minimal polynomial of $\operatorname{ad}(X_i)$ Since $1, T, T^p, T^{p^2}, \ldots, T^{p^n}$ are linearly independent in $k[T]/(m_i(T))$, we can find a p-polynomial $f_i(T) \in (m_i(T))$, $1 \leq i \leq n$. We may assume that

$\deg f_i = p^{r_i} \geqslant p$. Then $c_i = f_i(X_i)$ lies in the center of $U(L)$. It follows that the monomials

$$c_1^{a_1} \cdots c_n^{a_n} \cdot X_1^{b_1} \cdots X_n^{b_n} , \quad 0 \leqslant a_i < \infty , \quad 0 \leqslant b_i < p^{r_i},$$

form a k-basis of $U(L)$. If $M = U(L)/(c_1, \ldots, c_n)$, then M has as a k-basis, the monomials

$$X_1^{b_1} \cdots X_n^{b_n} , \quad 0 \leqslant b_i < p^{r_i} .$$

Thus the canonical map $L \to M$ is injective.

Using the notation of the above proof, let $J = (c_1^2, c_2, \ldots, c_n)$ and let $A = U(L)/J$. Then A is a finite dimensional associative k-algebra which is not semisimple, so it cannot be a direct sum of simple ideals, i.e., it cannot be a completely reducible L-module.

CHAPTER V

INVARIANTS OF AFFINE GROUPS

V-1 HILBERT'S FOURTEENTH PROBLEM

At the International Mathematical Congress in 1900, Hilbert proposed twenty-three problems whose solutions he hoped would be found in the twentieth century. Some of these have been solved and some have resisted all assaults. The fourteenth of these problems is the following.

> Let G be a subgroup of GL_n. If GL_n acts linearly on the variables $X_1,\ldots,X_n$ then G acts on $k[X_1,\ldots,X_n]$ as a group of k-algebra automorphisms. Is the ring of G-invariant elements of $k[X_1,\ldots,X_n]$ finitely generated?

Considerable progress has been made on this problem - in fact, the solution to the problem as stated is negative - a result presented by Nagata at the International Congress in 1958. We shall not give Nagata's counterexample here (cf., however, his Lectures on the Fourteenth Problem of Hilbert, Tata Institute, 1965). Rather we shall concentrate on the positive results connected with the problem.

Hilbert himself had already proved, in 1890, that the answer is affirmative if k is the complex number field and $G = SL_r$ embedded in GL_n, $n = \binom{r+d-1}{d}$ via the d-th symmetric power of the standard representation. This proof can be found in Weyl's book, The Classical Groups. An unsuccessful attempt at the general problem was made by Maurer in 1899, and another, based on Maurer's ideas, by Weitzenbock, in 1932. Weitzenbock's paper does however contain a correct proof if G is a 1-dimensional closed subgroup of GL_n. In 1911, Fischer solved the problem for the case where k is the complex number field and G is conjugate in GL_n to a subgroup G' with the property that $x \in G'$ implies ${}^t\bar{x} \in G'$, where $\bar{x}$ denotes the complex conjugate of x. All these results were for $k = \mathbf{C}$, the complex numbers. However, Nagata's counterexample holds in all characteristics, so the failure of finite generation is not due to characteristic p pathology.

Emmy Noether showed in 1916 that the answer is affirmative if G is a finite group and the characteristic is 0, and in 1926 that the same holds in any characteristic.

The most striking results in the positive direction are due to Weyl, who showed, as a consequence of his theorem on complete reducibility of representations of semisimple Lie algebras - that if k is the complex number field and G is semisimple, then finite generation holds. His original proof used the techniques of compact real Lie groups and the so-called "unitarian trick", which we shall not discuss. The most general results we have at present on finite generation are due to Nagata.

Although the problem is stated for arbitrary subgroups of GL_n, we need only consider closed subgroups because of the following.

LEMMA 5.1. Let G be an affine group and let M be a rational G-module. If H is a subgroup of G then $M^H = M^{\overline{H}}$.

<u>Proof</u>: First we show that if T is a subset of M then $S_o(T)$ is closed in G. $S_o(T)$ is clearly a subgroup of G. Now we know that $S_o(T) = \bigcap_{m \in T} S(m)$. Since M is a rational G-module, any $m \in M$ lies in a finite dimensional G-submodule N of M. But N may then be considered as a variety, viz., $N = \underline{A}^d$, $d = \dim N$, and we know that stabilizers for actions are closed by proposition 2.10. If $H' = S_o(M^H)$, then H' is closed and contains H,

so $M^{H'} \subset M^{\overline{H}} \subset M^{H}$. But $M^{H'} \supset M^{H}$ and the lemma follows.

It also turns out to be advantageous to allow more general rings than polynomial rings as our G-modules. The proper setup appears to be the following. Let G be an affine group and let R be a finitely generated k-algebra with G acting on R by k-algebra automorphisms. Then is R^G a finitely generated k-algebra? We show in this chapter that if G is linearly reductive, the answer is affirmative. In fact, we show that if G has a slightly weaker property than linear reductivity, then the answer is still yes. In the case of linearly reductive groups we prove that if G acts on an affine algebraic set V and the orbits of G are closed in V, then a strict quotient of V by G exists and is an affine algebraic set.

V-2 THE REYNOLDS OPERATOR

N.B. Throughout this section, G is assumed to be a linearly reductive affine group.

If M is a rational G-module, let us say that M is G-ergodic if $M^G = (0)$. We borrow this term from ergodic theory, altering the meaning slightly. The next result is absolutely critical.

LEMMA 5.2. Any rational G-module M contains a unique maximal G-ergodic submodule M_G. Moreover, $M = M^G \oplus M_G$ and M_G is the unique G-complement of M^G in M.

Proof: Note that the union of a chain of G-ergodic submodules of M is itself a G-ergodic submodule. Thus we may apply Zorn's lemma to find a maximal G-ergodic submodule M_o of M. To show that M_o is unique, let M' be a G-submodule of M such that $M' \not\subset M^G$. Then M' contains a finite dimensional simple submodule P on which G acts non-trivially. Since P is simple, it is G-ergodic. If $P \not\subset M_o$, then $P \cap M_o = (0)$, whence $P + M_o = P \oplus M_o$. From this it follows immediately that $P + M_o$ is G-ergodic, contradicting the maximality of M_o.

To prove the second assertion, note that $M^G \cap M_G = (0)$. On the other hand, if $M^G + M_G \neq M$, then there is a simple G-ergodic submodule Q such that $Q \not\subset M_G$, contradicting what was shown above.

Finally, if N is another G-complement of M^G, then, by what we have just shown, every simple submodule of N lies in M_G. By linear reductivity, every finite dimensional submodule of N is a sum of simple submodules. Since N is a rational G-module, $N \subset M_G$. But as N and M_G are both complements of M^G, we must have $N = M_G$. q.e.d.

REMARK. Notice that complete reducibility was only used in the proof of lemma 5.2 to prove uniqueness of the complement. However, as we shall now see, this uniqueness is the key to the kingdom.

DEFINITION 5.3. Let M be a rational G-module. We denote by P_M the projection of M onto M^G whose kernel is M_G. P_M is called the <u>Reynolds operator</u> of M.

From the uniqueness of the Reynolds operator, it follows that if $\eta : M \to M'$ is a G-homomorphism of rational G-modules, then $\eta \circ P_M = P_{M'} \circ \eta$.

Now let R be a k-algebra which is a rational G-module such that G acts on R by k-algebra automorphisms, i.e., $(fg)^x = f^x g^x$ for $f,g \in R$, $x \in G$. The result of the next lemma is known as Reynolds' identity.

LEMMA 5.4. If $f \in R$ and $g \in R^G$, then

$$P_R(gf) = gP_R(f) .$$

<u>Proof</u>: Since $P_R(g(f - P_R(f))) = P_R(gf) - gP_R(f)$, we may assume that $f \in R_G$. Then we must show that $P_R(gf) = 0$, i.e., $gf \in R_G$. But if M is a simple G-submodule of R_G then either gM is isomorphic to M or $gM = (0)$. In the former case, gM is ergodic, so in either case, $gM \subset R_G$.

LEMMA 5.5. If (I_j) is a collection of ideals in R, and each I_j is a G-submodule of R, then

$$(\sum_j I_j) \cap R^G = \sum_j (I_j \cap R^G) .$$

Proof: Clearly $\sum(I_j \cap R^G) \subset (\sum I_j) \cap R^G$. For the opposite inclusion, note that if

$$f \in (\sum I_j) \cap R^G ,$$

then $f = \sum f_j$, with $f_j \in I_j$ and the sum is finite. Then

$$P_R(f) = \sum P_R(f_j) \in \sum (I_j \cap R^G) ,$$

since $P_R | M = P_M$ for any G-submodule M of R.

LEMMA 5.6. Let S be any commutative R^G-algebra. Then G operates by S-algebra automorphisms on $R \otimes_{R^G} S$ and the action is rational. Moreover,

$$(R \otimes_{R^G} S)^G = S .$$

Proof: The action of G on $R \otimes_{R^G} S$ is defined by: $(f \otimes g)^x = f^x \otimes g$, $f \in R$, $g \in S$. The first assertion is now clear. To see that the action is rational, let $h = \sum f_i \otimes g_i$ be an element of $R \otimes_{R^G} S$. If M is a finite dimensional G-submodule of R containing all the f_i, then $\sum M \otimes_k kg_i$ is a finite dimensional G-submodule of $R \otimes_k S$ which maps onto a G-submodule of $R \otimes_{R^G} S$ containing h.

For the last assertion, let $P = P_R$ and $P' = P_{R \otimes_{R^G} S}$. If $h = \sum f_i \otimes g_i \in (R \otimes_{R^G} S)^G$ then

$$\begin{aligned} h &= P'(\sum f_i \otimes g_i) = \\ &P'(\sum (f_i \otimes 1)(1 \otimes g_i)) = \\ &\sum (1 \otimes g_i) P'(f_i \otimes 1) = \\ &\sum P(f_i) \otimes g_i = \\ &1 \otimes (\sum g_i P(f_i)) \in S . \end{aligned}$$

LEMMA 5.7. Let $R = \bigoplus_{i \geq 0} R_i$ be a graded ring such that the ideal $R_+ = \bigoplus_{i > 0} R_i$ has a finite basis. Then R is a finitely generated R_o-algebra. In particular, if R_o is noetherian, then R is noetherian if and only if R is a finitely generated R_o-algebra.

<u>Proof</u>: Let $f_1, \ldots, f_r$ be a homogeneous ideal basis for R_+, i.e., $f_i \in R_{d_i}$. Then for large n, we have $R_n = \sum f_i R_{n-d_i}$. Therefore R is generated as R_o-algebra by $f_1, \ldots, f_r$ and $R_{n-d_1} + \cdots + R_{n-d_r}$ for some fixed n. Thus it suffices to prove that each R_i is a finitely generated R_o-module.

If this is false, let p be minimal such that R_p is not a finitely generated R_o-module and let $R' = R/\bigoplus_{i > p} R_i$. If $M = \sum_{\substack{r+s=p \\ rs \neq 0}} R'_r R'_s$ then M is an ideal in R' and if $R'' = R'/M$, then $R''_+ = \bigoplus_{i>0} R''_i$ has a finite ideal basis. But $R''_+ R''_p = (0)$ so that R''_p is a finitely generated module over $R''/R''_+ = R_o$. If $g_1, \ldots, g_t$ generate R''_p over R_o, then $R'_p = M + \sum R_o g_i$ so that R'_p is a finitely generated R_o-module. As R'_p is isomorphic to R_p, we have a contradiction.

If R_o is noetherian and R is a finitely generated R_o-algebra, then R is noetherian by corollary 1.14. If R is noetherian, then R_+ has a finite ideal basis and so R is a finitely generated R_o-algebra.

V-3 MUMFORD'S THEOREM

This is:

THEOREM 5.8. Let G be a linearly reductive affine group and let V be an affine algebraic set. Let α be an action of G on V over k. Then a quotient of V by G exists. If the orbits of α in V are closed, then this quotient is a strict quotient.

We shall prove the theorem in several steps. The following is the most important step - just as in the proof of theorem 2.26. Note that we prove more than is required for theorem 5.8, i.e., we allow nilpotent elements in our k-algebras.

THEOREM 5.9. Let G be a linearly reductive affine group and let R be a finitely generated k-algebra. Let G act rationally on R by k-algebra automorphisms. Then R^G is a finitely generated k-algebra.

<u>Proof</u>: Let I be an ideal of R^G and let $S = R^G/I$. Then $R \otimes_{R^G} S = R/IR$. By lemma 5.6, $(R/IR)^G = R^G/I$, whence $IR \cap R^G = I$. Now if (I_j) is an ascending chain of ideals in R^G, then (I_jR) is an ascending chain of ideals in R. Since R is noetherian, (I_jR) terminates, whence (I_j) terminates. Therefore R^G is noetherian.

Next, assume that R is graded and that G acts homogeneously, i.e., each R_i is a G-submodule of R. Then if $R = \bigoplus_{i>0} R_i$, we have $R^G = \bigoplus_{i>0} R_i^G$ so that R^G is also graded. Then, by lemma 5.7, R^G is a finitely generated k-algebra.

In the general case, let M be a finite dimensional G-submodule of R containing a set of generators for R over k. Then G acts rationally and homogeneously on the symmetric algebra $S(M)$ so that $S(M)^G$ is finitely generated. There is a surjective G-homomorphism of k-algebras $\varphi : S(M) \rightarrow R$. If $f \in S(M)$ then $P_R(\varphi(f)) = \varphi(P_{S(M)}(f))$. Therefore maps $S(M)^G$ onto R^G and hence R^G is finitely generated.

To prove the first assertion of theorem 5.8, we

apply theorem 5.9 to $k[V]$. Let V_o be an affine model of $k[V]^G$. Then if $\varphi : V \to V_o$ is the k-morphism induced by the inclusion, we see immediately that (V_o, φ) is a quotient of V by G.

The second assertion has much more geometric content, and we must work harder to prove it. Condition iii) of definition 2.15 is evidently fulfilled. Now by lemma 5.5, if (W_i) is a family of closed invariant subsets of V, then

$$\overline{\varphi(\bigcap_i W_i)} = \bigcap_i \overline{\varphi W_i} .$$

Let W be a closed invariant subset of V and let v be a point of V_o. Let $W' = \varphi^{-1}(v)$. Then

$$\overline{\varphi(W \cap W')} = \overline{\varphi W} \cap \{v\} .$$

Thus if $v \in \overline{\varphi W}$, then $W \cap W' \neq \emptyset$, i.e., $v \in \varphi W$. Therefore φW is closed. It follows that if Z is a subset of V_o then Z is closed if and only if $\varphi^{-1} Z$ is closed. This proves ii) of 2.15.

Condition i) is the most subtle, for _a priori_, we do not know that V_o does not consist of a single point. However, if W and W' are closed invariant subsets of V, then by lemma 5.5, we have

$$(\underline{I}_V(W) + \underline{I}_V(W')) \cap k[V_o] =$$
$$(\underline{I}_V(W) \cap k[V_o]) + (\underline{I}_V(W') \cap k[V_o]) .$$

If W and W' are disjoint, then $\underline{I}_V(W) + \underline{I}_V(W') = k[V]$ so that we can write $1 = f + g$ with

$f \in \underline{I}_V(W) \cap k[V_o]$, $g \in \underline{I}_V(W') \cap k[V_o]$. This means that there is an invariant function which vanishes on W and is identically 1 on W'. Since the orbits are closed, it follows that for each $v \in V_o$, $\varphi^{-1}(v)$ contains at most one orbit. On the other hand, V itself is a closed invariant subset of V and so φV is closed in V_o. Since $k[V_o]$ is a subring of $k[V]$, φV is dense in V_o. Therefore φ is surjective. q.e.d.

COMPLEMENT 5.10. If V is a variety, so is V_o.

Notice that the quotient of an affine algebraic set by a linearly reductive affine group is always an affine algebraic set. We have remarked before that quotients may exist and not be affine. Note also that theorem 5.9 provides an affirmative solution to Hilbert's fourteenth problem for linearly reductive groups - in particular for semisimple groups in characteristic zero.

V-4 SEMISIMPLE GROUPS REVISITED

We have said that an affine group G is semisimple if its Lie algebra $\underline{g}$ is semisimple and the characteristic is zero. Our purpose in this section is to give a definition for semisimplicity in any characteristic and to show that this definition agrees with definition 4.36 in characteristic zero.

PROPOSITION 5.11. Let G be a connected affine group. Then there exists a unique maximal normal connected solvable subgroup R of G. Moreover, R is a closed subgroup of G.

Proof: Suppose that H and K are solvable normal subgroups of G. Then HK is a normal subgroup of G, for if $h,h' \in H$ and $k,k' \in K$, then $hk(h'k')^{-1} = h(kk'^{-1})h'^{-1} = h(kk'^{-1})h^{-1}hh'^{-1} = h"k"$, with $h" \in H$, $k" \in K$. But $HK = KH$ because $hk = kk^{-1}hk = kh_1$. Therefore HK is a subgroup. Also, $xhkx^{-1} = xhx^{-1}xkx^{-1} = h_o k_o$ so that HK is normal. Since HK is a continuous image of $H \times K$, it is connected if both H and K are connected. Since HK/K is isomorphic to $H/H \cap K$, it follows that HK is solvable if both H and K are solvable. We need to show that if H and K are closed, then HK is closed. This will follow from the general:

LEMMA 5.12. Let G be an affine group and let $V_1,\ldots,V_r$ be subsets of G such that

i) $e \in V_i$ for all i,

ii) $\overline{V}_i$ is a subvariety of G for each i,

iii) V_i contains a non-empty open subset of $\overline{V}_i$ for each i.

Then the subgroup H generated by $V_1,\ldots,V_r$ is

closed in G.

Proof: Let $V = \prod \overline{V}_i \times \prod \overline{V}_i^{-1}$. Then V is an affine variety and $\prod V_i \times \prod V_i^{-1}$ contains a non-empty open subset of V. If U is a subset of G, we denote by $U^{[n]}$ the image of U^n under the product morphism $G^n \to G$. Set $V_o = V_1 \cdots V_r V_1^{-1} \cdots V_r^{-1}$. Then $V_o^{[n]}$ contains a non-empty open subset of $\overline{V^{[n]}}$ and $\overline{V^{[n]}}$ is a subvariety of G. Since $e \in V_i$, we have $V^{[n]} \subset V^{[n+1]}$ for n sufficiently large. Therefore $\overline{H} = \overline{V^{[n]}}$ for n large. Hence $(V_o^{[n]})^{[2]} = \overline{H}$ for large n. Since $V_o^{[n]} \subset H$, it follows that H is closed.

COROLLARY 5.13. If G is an affine group, then the commutator subgroup (G,G) is closed in G. If G is connected, then (G,G) is connected.

Proof: Apply the lemma to V = image of $G \times G$ under $(x,y) \mapsto xyx^{-1}y^{-1}$ to see that (G,G) is closed. If G is connected, set $V_o = VV^{-1}$. Then V is connected, so V_o, and hence $V_o^{[n]}$, is connected. Therefore (G,G) is connected.

REMARK. It follows by a similar argument that any verbal subgroup of a (connected) affine group is closed (and connected).

DEFINITION 5.14. Let G be a connected affine group. We let the radical $R(G)$ of G be the maximal connected normal solvable subgroup of G.

DEFINITION 5.15. We say that a connected affine group G is semisimple if $R(G) = (e)$. We say that G is solvable (resp., nilpotent) if it is solvable (resp., nilpotent) as an abstract group.

The following analogue of Lie's theorem is due to Kolchin. Note that, for groups, we do not need to assume that the characteristic is zero.

THEOREM 5.16. Let G be a connected solvable affine group and let M be a rational G-module. Then G has an eigenvector in M, i.e., there exists a non-zero $m \in M$ such that km is a G-submodule of M.

As in the case of Lie's theorem, the proof is based on an interesting lemma. First note that if H is a subgroup of G and $m \in M$ is an eigenvector of H, then $xm = \chi(x)m$ for all $x \in H$. The mapping χ from H to G_m is called a (rational) character of H. It is clearly a homomorphism. Note also that if M is finite dimensional - which is the only case we need to consider - then the number of distinct characters of H which arise in this way from M is finite. To see this, note that if $m_1, \ldots, m_r$ is a maximal independent set of eigenvectors of H in

M and $\chi_1,\ldots,\chi_r$ are the corresponding characters, then if m is an eigenvector of H with character χ, we must have $m = \sum a_i m_i$ and $xm = \sum a_i xm_i$, so that $a_i \chi(x) = a_i \chi_i(x)$ for all i, and all $x \in H$. Thus χ is one of the χ_i.

LEMMA 5.17. Let G be a connected affine group and let H be a normal subgroup of G. If M is a finite dimensional rational G-module and $m \in M$ is an eigenvector of H with character χ, then $\chi(x^{-1}yx) = \chi(y)$ for all $x \in G$, $y \in H$.

<u>Proof</u>: If n is an eigenvector, let χ_n denote it character. Then we have

$$yxm = xx^{-1}yxm = x\chi_m(x^{-1}yx)m = \chi_m(x^{-1}yx)xm ,$$

so that $\chi_{xm}(y) = \chi_m(x^{-1}yx)$. Since there are only a finite number of characters of the form χ_{xm}, $x \in G$, the subgroup $K = \{x \in G : \chi_{xm} = \chi_m\}$ has finite index in G. Now for each $y \in H$ we let $f_y(x) = \chi_{xm}(y) - \chi_m(y)$. Since M is a rational G-module, each f_y lies in k[G]. If I is the ideal in k[G] generated by the f_y, $y \in H$, then $K = \underline{V}_G(I)$. Thus K is closed, so that K = G.

To prove the theorem, note that by corollary 5.13 (G,G) is connected. Using induction on the length of the derived series of G, we may assume that the theorem is true for (G,G).

If m_o is an eigenvector of (G,G), then by lemma 5.17, the set of $m \in M$ such that $ym = \chi_{m_o}(y)m$ for all $y \in (G,G)$ is a G-submodule of M. As it suffices to prove the theorem when M is G-simple, we may assume that $ym = \chi_{m_o}(y)m$ for all $m \in M$, $y \in (G,G)$. If $x \in G$, let H be the subgroup of G generated by x and (G,G). If m_1 is an eigenvector for x, then it is an eigenvector for H. Since H is normal in G, we can apply lemma 5.17 to deduce that the set of all $m \in M$ such that $ym = \chi_{m_1}(y)m$ for all $y \in H$ is a G-submodule of M, and hence all of M. Thus $xm \in km$ for all $m \in M$. Since this holds for any $x \in G$ and since M is simple, it follows that $\dim M = 1$, as required.

REMARK. Note the similarity between the proofs of theorems 4.15 and 5.16. Actually, theorem 5.16 is a very special case of the famous Borel fixed point theorem, which asserts that if a connected solvable affine group acts on a <u>complete</u> variety, then there is a fixed point. Theorem 5.16 follows by applying this to the projective space associated to M.

EXERCISE. Recall that a <u>flag</u> in a finite dimensional vector space M is a sequence of subspaces, $(0) = M_o < M_1 < M_2 < \cdots < M_n = M$ such that $\dim M_i/M_{i-1} = 1$.

Show that if L is a Lie subalgebra of $\underline{gl}(M)$ which stabilizes a flag in M, then L is solvable. From this, deduce that the Lie algebra of a solvable affine group is solvable.

LEMMA 5.18. Let G be a connected affine group. If k has characteristic zero and $\underline{g}$ is solvable, then G is solvable.

Proof: First we show that if M is a rational G-module, then G has an eigenvector in M. Since $\underline{g}$ is solvable and the characteristic is zero, $\underline{g}$ has an eigenvector $m \in M$. Then km is a $\underline{g}$-submodule of M, hence also a G-submodule, i.e., m is an eigenvector of G. Next, if G is a closed subgroup of GL_n then repeated application of the first step yields a flag in $\underline{A}^n$ stabilized by G. Thus, for a suitable basis of $\underline{A}^n$, G will be represented by triangular matrices. Therefore G is solvable.

LEMMA 5.19. Let L be a semisimple Lie algebra over k. If k has characteristic zero, then every k-derivation of L is inner, i.e., $ad : L \to Der_k(L)$ is surjective, and hence an isomorphism.

Proof: Since the Killing form of L is non-degenerate, $\ker(ad) = (0)$. Now if $D \in Der_k(L)$ then $D[X,Y] = [DX,Y] + [X,DY]$ for all $X,Y \in L$. Thus $ad(DX) = [D,ad(X)]$ for all $X \in L$ so that L is an ideal in $\mathrm{Der}_k(L)$. Applying complete reducibility to $\mathrm{Der}_k(L)$, we obtain a subspace L' of $\mathrm{Der}_k(L)$ which is complementary to L in $\mathrm{Der}_k(L)$ and such that $\mathrm{ad}(X)L' \subset L'$ for all $X \in L$. Now $[L,L'] \subset L$ as L is an ideal, and $[L,L'] \subset L'$ since L' is stable under ad. Therefore $[L,L'] = (0)$. But as L has no center, it follows that L' is the annihilator of L and hence is an ideal in $\mathrm{Der}_k(L)$. Now if $D \in L'$, then $\mathrm{ad}(DX) = [D,\mathrm{ad}(X)] = 0$ for all $X \in L$. Hence $DX = 0$ for all $X \in L$, i.e., $L' = (0)$.

EXERCISE. Let A be a finite dimensional (not necessarily associative) k-algebra. Then $\mathrm{Aut}_k(A)$ is an affine group. Show that the Lie algebra of $\mathrm{Aut}_k(A)$ is $\mathrm{Der}_k(A)$.

THEOREM 5.20. If k has characteristic zero and G is a connected affine group, then $\underline{r}(\underline{g})$ is the Lie algebra of $R(G)$.

<u>Proof</u>: Let $\overline{\underline{g}} = \underline{g}/\underline{r}(\underline{g})$ and let $\overline{\mathrm{Ad}} : G \to \mathrm{Aut}(\overline{\underline{g}})$ be the induced rational representation. Then the exact sequence of affine groups

$$(1) \to \ker \overline{\mathrm{Ad}} \longrightarrow G \xrightarrow{\overline{\mathrm{Ad}}} \mathrm{Aut}(\overline{\underline{g}})_o$$

yields an exact sequence of Lie algebras

$$0 \to \underline{h} \to \underline{g} \xrightarrow{\alpha} \underline{\mathrm{Aut}}(\overline{\underline{g}}) = \mathrm{Der}_k(\overline{\underline{g}}) .$$

Since $\bar{\underline{g}}$ is semisimple, α is surjective, by lemma 5.19. If $\overline{Ad}$ is not surjective then the image is a closed subgroup of $Aut(\bar{\underline{g}})$. If we know that the dimension of the image is less than $\dim Aut(\bar{\underline{g}})$ then we get a contradiction to the surjectivity of α. Assuming this, we see that $\underline{h}$ is the Lie algebra of $\ker \overline{Ad}$. Since $\bar{\underline{g}}$ is semisimple, $\underline{h} = \underline{r}(\underline{g})$. Applying lemma 5.18, we see that $(\ker \overline{Ad})_o$ is the radical of G.

Let $G' = \overline{Ad}(G)$. To show that $\dim G' = \dim Aut$ implies $\overline{Ad}$ surjective, we note the following general fact. If V and V' are varieties such that $\dim V = \dim V'$ and if $\eta : k[V] \longrightarrow k[V']$ is a surjective k-algebra homomorphism, then η is an isomorphism. To see this, let $u_1,\ldots,u_n$ be a transcendence basis for $k(V')$ over k, with $u_i \in k[V']$. Choose $v_i \in k[V]$ such that $\eta(v_i) = u_i$, $1 \leqslant i \leqslant n$. Then the v_i are evidently algebraically independent over k so that they form a transcendence basis for $k(V)$ over k. If f is a non-zero element of $k[V]$, then f is algebraic over $k(v)$ so we have a minimal equation $\sum g_i(v)f^i = 0$, $g_i \in k[v] = k[v_1,\ldots,v_n]$ and $g_o \neq 0$. If $\eta(f) = 0$, then $\sum g_i(u)\eta(f)^i = 0$ so that $g_o(u) = 0$ which is a contradiction. Thus $\ker \eta = (0)$ and the theorem is proved.

COROLLARY 5.21. Definitions 4.36 and 5.15 agree in characteristic zero.

V-5 SOLVABLE GROUPS

In this section we examine the structure of solvable affine groups. We define the unipotent radical of an affine group and the notion of reductivity for affine groups. It will then follow immediately from what we have already proved that in characteristic zero, a reductive affine group is linearly reductive.

DEFINITION 5.22. An affine group is called a <u>torus</u> if it is k-isomorphic to a product of copies of G_m.

PROPOSITION 5.23. Let G be a connected affine group. The following are equivalent.

i) Every rational G-module is diagonalizable, i.e., there exists a basis consisting of eigenvectors of G.

ii) There exists a faithful rational G-module which is diagonalizable.

iii) G is k-isomorphic to a closed subgroup of a torus.

<u>Proof</u>: Clearly i) implies ii) and ii) implies iii). If G is a closed subgroup of $D = G_m^d$, then we have a surjective homomorphism $\eta : k[D] \longrightarrow k[G]$, which is a homomorphism of rational G-modules. Since every finite dimensional rational G-module is isomorphic to

a submodule of a direct sum of copies of $k[G]$, it suffices to show that $k[G]$ is a diagonalizable G-module, and for this it is enough to show that $k[D]$ is a diagonalizable D-module. If $s = (s_1,\ldots,s_d) \in D$, then as $k[D] = k[X_1,\ldots,X_d,X_1^{-1},\ldots,X_d^{-1}]$ and

$$(X_1^{n_1}\cdots X_d^{n_d})^s = s_1^{n_1}\cdots s_d^{n_d} X_1^{n_1}\cdots X_d^{n_d},$$

where $n_i \in \mathbf{Z}$, we get what we want.

COROLLARY 5.24. If G is a closed subgroup of a torus, then G is linearly reductive - in any characteristic.

Proof: Let M be a finite dimensional rational G-module and let N be a G-submodule of M. We use induction on $\dim M - \dim N$. If $N \neq M$, choose a 1-dimensional G-submodule N_o of M with $N_o \not\subset N$. Then $N + N_o = N \oplus N_o$ and we can find a G-complement for $N + N_o$, etc.

If G is a group, let $G(n) = \{x \in G : x^n = e\}$. Set $G(*) = \bigcup_n G(n)$. Thus $G(*)$ is the set of elements of finite order in G.

PROPOSITION 5.25. If G is a closed subgroup of a torus then $G(*)$ is dense in G.

Proof: Since $G_m(*)$ is an infinite subset of G_m,

it is dense in G_m. Now if $G \subset G_m^d$ then the projection onto the i-th factor is a k-homomorphism, so the image of G is either finite or is the whole factor. Therefore $G(*)$ is a finite intersection of dense subsets of G and hence is dense.

Recall that a <u>rational character</u> of an affine group G is a k-homomorphism $\chi: G \to G_m$. We denote the set of rational characters of G by $\hat{G}$. Note that $\hat{G}$ is a group - under the multiplication $\chi\chi'(x) = \chi(x)\chi'(x)$. We will however follow custom and write the product in G additively so that $(\chi + \chi')(x) = \chi(x)\,\chi'(x)$. Now $\hat{G}_m$ is canonically isomorphic to $\mathbf{Z}$, as one sees by noting that $U(k[G_m]) = \{aX^n : n \in \mathbf{Z},\ a \in k,\ a \neq 0\}$. From this it follows immediately that if G is an n-dimensional torus, then $\hat{G} = \mathbf{Z}^n$.

PROPOSITION 5.26. Every closed subgroup of a torus is an intersection of the kernels of a finite number of rational characters of the torus.

<u>Proof</u>: Let D be a torus and let G be a closed subgroup of D. By corollary 2.21, there is a rational D-module M such that $G = \ker(D \to GL(M))$. Since M is a diagonalizable D-module, the proposition follows immediately.

COROLLARY 5.27. A connected closed subgroup of a torus is itself a torus.

Proof: Let D be a torus and let G be a connected closed subgroup of D. For any subset S of D, let $S^{o} = \{\chi \in \hat{D} : (S,\chi) = (1)\}$, and for any subset S' of $\hat{D}$, let $S'^{o} = \{x \in D : (x,S') = (1)\}$. Then by the proposition, $G = (G^{o})^{o}$. If p is the characteristic, then D/G^{o} is an abelian group with no p-torsion, for $(x,\chi)^{p} = 1$ implies $(x,\chi) = 1$. Therefore we can find a **Z**-basis $\chi_1,\ldots,\chi_r$ of $\hat{D}$ and integers $n_1,\ldots,n_s$, $s \leqslant r$, n_i prime to p, such that $n_1\chi_1,\ldots,n_s\chi_s$ form a **Z**-basis of G^{o}. The basis (χ_i) defines an isomorphism of D with G_m^r and $G = (G^{o})^{o}$ is isomorphic to $G_m(n_1) \times \cdots \times G_m(n_s) \times G_m^{r-s}$. Since G is connected, $n_1 = \cdots = n_s = 1$.

DEFINITION 5.28. Let G be an affine group and let M be a rational G-module. We say that $x \in G$ is <u>unipotent</u> on M if all the eigenvalues of x on M are 1.

PROPOSITION 5.29. Let G be an affine group and let x be an element of G. The following are equivalent.

i) x is unipotent on every rational G-module.

ii) There is a faithful rational G-module

on which x is unipotent.

iii) (characteristic 0) There is a k-morphism $\alpha : G_a \to G$ such that $x \in \alpha G_a$.
(characteristic p) $x^{p^n} = e$ for some n.

<u>Proof</u>: That i) implies ii) is obvious. Now if $G \subset GL_r$, then if x is unipotent, we can write $x = 1 + n$ with n nilpotent. To see that ii) implies iii), in characteristic zero, consider the mapping $\exp(tn_o)$ of G_a into GL_r. This is a k-homomorphism if n_o is nilpotent, as the exponential series becomes a polynomial. I claim that x lies in the image for a suitable choice of n_o. To show this, we must solve the system of equations

$$n_{ij} = t(n_o)_{ij} + (t^2/2)(n_o^2)_{ij} + \ldots + (t^r/r!)(n_o^r)_{ij}$$

$$1 \leqslant i,j \leqslant r, \quad i > j,$$

for t. There are $\binom{r}{2}$ of these equations and we seek $\binom{r}{2}$ coefficients with the property that the given equations have a common solution, t. This can evidently be done. Thus we may assume that 1 and x lie in the image. Since G_a has no closed subgroups but (0) and G_a in characteristic zero, it follows that the image lies in G, for if G' is the image, then either $G \cap G' = (1)$ or $G' \subset G$ and in the former case, we must have $x = 1$.

That ii) implies iii) in characteristic p is an immediate consequence of the binomial theorem.

To see that iii) implies i), it suffices to show in characteristic zero that every element of G_a is unipotent on every rational G_a-module M. Since G_a is commutative, it follows that the representation of G_a in M can be triangularized. Thus we must show that if dim M = 1, then M is G_a-trivial. But there is no k-homomorphism from G_a to the multiplicative group but the trivial one, as there is no polynomial f(T) such that f(a + b) = f(a)f(b) for all $a,b \in k$ except the trivial ones 0 and 1. In characteristic p, the hypothesis of iii) implies that all the eigenvalues are 1.

DEFINITION 5.30. Let G be an affine group. We say that $x \in G$ is <u>semisimple</u> if x is diagonalizable on every rational G-module. By 5.23, this is equivalent to saying that x is diagonalizable on some faithful rational G-module, or that x lies in a diagonalizabl subgroup of G.

It follows then that if $\varphi : G \to G'$ is a k-homomorphism of affine groups then $\varphi(x)$ is semisimple if x is semisimple, and $\varphi(x)$ is unipotent if x is unipotent.

THEOREM 5.31. Let G be an affine group. Every $x \in G$ can be written uniquely in the form $x = x_s x_u$ wher x_s is semisimple, x_u is unipotent, and x_s and

x_u commute.

<u>Proof</u>: We may assume that G is a closed subgroup of GL_r. By lemma 4.17, we can find a semisimple matrix x_s and a nilpotent matrix n such that $x = x_s + n$, x_s and n commute, and the decomposition is unique. Put $x_u = 1 + x_s^{-1}n$. Then $x_s^{-1}n$ is nilpotent because x_s and n commute. Therefore, x_u is unipotent, x_s and x_u commute, and $x = x_s x_u$. It remains to prove that x_s and x_u lie in G.

We may replace G by the smallest closed subgroup containing x. Since the center of the centralizer of x is closed, we may assume that G is commutative. If $G_s = \{x_s : x \in G\}$, then G_s is a commutative set of semisimple matrices. Thus we can find a flag (L_i) in $\underline{A}^r$ which is stable under $G \cup G_s$. Since G_s generates a semisimple subalgebra of $M_r(k)$, L_i is G_s-complemented in L_{i+1}. Thus we may assume that $G \subset T_r$ - the group of triangular matrices - and for each $x \in G$, $x_s \in D_r$ - the group of diagonal matrices. The map $x \mapsto x_s$ of G into D_r is a k-homomorphism which we denote by S. SG is closed in D_r and $SG(*)$ is dense in SG.

Now if $x \in G$ and $x_s^n = 1$, then $x^n = x_s^n x_u^n = x_u^n$ so that $x_u^n \in G$. If the characteristic is zero or if n is prime to p, then x_u and x_u^n generate the same subgroup of GL_r so that $x_u^n \in G$ implies $x_u \in G$. Then $x_s = x^{-1}x_u \in G$. Thus $SG \cap G$ is dense in

SG so that $SG \subset G$.

Note the similarity of this result to 4.17, which is the starting point of the proof. We observe that the decomposition of the theorem commutes with k-homomorphisms and that for any affine group G we have $G = G_u G_s = G_s G_u$, $G_s \cap G_u = (e)$, where G_s (resp., G_u) denotes the set of semisimple (resp., unipotent) elements of G. In general, neither G_s nor G_u is a subgroup of G, but for solvable groups, we have:

PROPOSITION 5.32. If G is a connected solvable affine group, then G_u is a closed normal subgroup of G and G/G_u is a torus.

<u>Proof</u>: We may assume that $G \subset T_n$. Then $G_u = G \cap U_n$ where U_n is the set of unipotent matrices in T_n. Since U_n is a closed normal subgroup of T_n, the first assertion follows. On the other hand, since G is connected, G/G_u is connected and every element of G/G_u is the image of a semisimple element of G, whence G/G_u is diagonalizable.

REMARK. If G is any connected affine group, one defines the <u>unipotent</u> <u>radical</u> of G to be $R(G)_u$. One says that G is <u>reductive</u> if $R(G)_u = (e)$, i.e., if R(G) is a torus. If k has characteristic 0, theorem 4.40 shows that a reductive group is linearly reductive.

LEMMA 5.33. Let M be a finite dimensional k-vector space and let Z be a subset of $End_k(M)$. If M is Z-simple, i.e., no non-trivial subspace of M is stable under all elements of Z, then Z spans $End_k(M)$.

Proof: Clearly M is Z-simple if and only if M^* is Z^*-simple. If there exists a non-zero F in $End_k(M)^*$ such that $F(Z) = (0)$, then $A^*F = \lambda(A)F$ for all $A \in Z$, where $\lambda(A) \in k$, i.e., F is an eigenvector of $Z^* \subset End_k(M)^* = End_k(M^*)$. If F is nilpotent on M^* then the image of F is a Z^*-subspace and if F is not nilpotent on M^* then any eigenvector of F is an eigenvector of Z^*.

THEOREM 5.34. Let G be a connected unipotent affine group, i.e., $G = G_u$, and let M be a non-zero rational G-module. Then $M^G \neq (0)$.

Proof: We may assume that M is G-simple and that $G \subset GL(M)$. Then, by lemma 5.33, G spans $End_k(M)$. Now if $x = 1 + n \in G$, then $Tr_M(x) = Tr_M(1) + Tr_M(n) = Tr_M(1)$ as n is nilpotent. If $y \in G$, then $Tr_M(ny) = Tr_M((x - 1)y) = Tr_M(xy) - Tr_M(y) = 0$. As G spans $End_k(M)$, it follows that $Tr_M(nz) = 0$ for all z $End_k(M)$, i.e., $n = 0$. Thus G acts trivially on M.

COROLLARY 5.35. A connected unipotent affine group is solvable.

PROPOSITION 5.37. A connected 1-dimensional affine group is commutative.

Proof: Let G act on itself by inner automorphisms. If G is not commutative, then at least one orbit is open, and the complement of this orbit is the center Z of G. Passing to G/Z we may assume that all non-trivial elements of G are conjugate. Thus G/Z is either diagonalizable or unipotent. In the first case, G/Z is a torus and in the second, it is a solvable group, whence $(G/Z,G/Z) = (e)$. In either case, G/Z is commutative, which is a contradiction. Therefore G is commutative.

REMARK. Actually if G is 1-dimensional and connected, then either $G = G_u$ or $G = G_s$. If $G \neq G_u$, the since G_u is a closed subgroup of G and G/G_u is a torus, it follows that G_s must be dense in G. If $G \subset GL_n$, we may assume that $G_s \subset D_n$, whence $G \subset D_n$ and $G_u = (e)$.

One can go much further and show that any 1-dimensional connected affine group is isomorphic to either G_a or G_m according to whether G is unipotent or diagonalizable.

V-6 INTEGRAL DEPENDENCE AND FINITENESS

Although the results of this section - like those of I-3 - are part of the standard algebraic backgroun we digress to prove them here because of their critical importance for invariant theory, and because many of these results arose in that context. For simplicity, we make a noetherian assumption which is not indispensable.

DEFINITION 5.38. Let R be a ring and let S be a ring containing R - both commutative and with the same identity. An element $f \in S$ is said to be <u>integral</u> over R if there is a monic polynomial F $R[X]$ such that $F(f) = 0$.

LEMMA 5.39. Let R and S be as in 5.38 and assume that R is noetherian. Then $f \in S$ is integral over R if and only if $R[f]$ is a finitely generated R-module.

<u>Proof</u>: If $f^n + a_{n-1}f^{n-1} + \ldots + a_1 f + a_o = 0$, with $a_i \in R$, then all of the f^i with $i \geqslant n$ can be expressed as linear combinations of $1, f, f^2, \ldots, f^{n-1}$, with coefficients in R. Conversely, assume that $R[f]$ is a finitely generated R-module. Let N_n be the submodule generated by $1, f, f^2, \ldots, f^n$. Then (N_n) is an ascending chain of submodules of $R[f]$ and $R[f] = \bigcup_n N_n$. By the a.c.c., $R[f] = N_n$ for some n, i.e., $f^{n+1} + a_n f^n + \ldots + a_1 f + a_o = 0$, for suitable $a_i \in R$.

COROLLARY 5.40. If $f_1,\ldots,f_r \in S$, then $f_1,\ldots,f_r$ are integral over R if and only if $R[f_1,\ldots,f_r]$ is a finitely generated R-module.

LEMMA 5.41. The set of $f \in S$ which are integral over R is a subring of S containing R.

<u>Proof</u>: Since every $f \in R$ is a solution of $X - f = 0$, every element of R is integral over R. If f and g are elements of S integral over R, then R[f,g] is a finitely generated R-module. Thus R[f + g] and R[fg] are finitely generated R-modules.

LEMMA 5.42. Let R and S be as above. If R' is a subring of S every element of which is integral over R and if $f \in S$ is integral over R', then f is integral over R.

Proof: Let R" be the subring of S obtained by adjoining to R the coefficients of a fixed integral dependence relation for f over R. Then f is integral over R" and R" is a finitely generated R-module, by 5.40. Thus R"[f] is a finitely generated R-module and hence so is R[f].

DEFINITION 5.43. If R is a (noetherian) ring and S is an overring of R with the same identity, the ring R' of elements of S integral over R is called the <u>integral</u> <u>closure</u> of R in S.

If R'' is a subring of S lying between R and R', we say that R'' is integral over R in S. It is not true in general that the integral closure of a noetherian ring in an overring is noetherian. For examples, see: M. Nagata, Local Rings, (Interscience).

The next result is known as the Noether normalization lemma.

THEOREM 5.44. Let $R = k[x_1,\ldots,x_n]$ be a domain. Then there exist algebraically independent elements $y_1,\ldots,y_d$ in R such that R is integral over $k[y_1,\ldots,y_d]$.

Proof: Let d be the transcendence degree of the field $k(x_1,\ldots,x_n)$ over k. If $d = n$, then the x_i are algebraically independent and we are done. Using induction on $n - d$, we need only prove that we can find elements $z_1,\ldots,z_{n-1}$ in R such that R is integral over $k[z_1,\ldots,z_{n-1}]$. Assuming $n > d$, let $f(x_1,\ldots,x_n) = 0$ be an algebraic dependence relation among the x_i. Set $z_i = x_i - x_1^{r_i}$, $2 \leqslant i \leqslant n$, where the integers r_i are to be determined. Then

$$f(x_1, z_2 + x_1^{r_2},\ldots,z_n + x_1^{r_n}) = 0 .$$

If the r_i are large enough and if they increase rapidly enough, then

$$f(x_1, z_2 + x_1^{r_2},\ldots,z_n + x_1^{r_n}) = ax_1^N + (\text{terms of deg.} < N),$$

with $a \in k$, $a \neq 0$. If we multiply through by $1/a$ we see that x_1 is integral over $k[z_2,\ldots,z_n]$.

DEFINITION 5.45. Let R be a (noetherian) domain and let K be its fraction field. We say that R is <u>normal</u> or <u>integrally closed</u> if R is its own integral closure in K.

LEMMA 5.46. Let R be a (noetherian) unique factorization domain. Then R is normal.

<u>Proof</u>: Let $f \in K$ be integral over R. If $f = g/h$ with $g,h \in R$, we have $(g/h)^n + a_{n-1}(g/h)^{n-1} + \ldots + a_o = 0$, $a_i \in R$. This gives

$$g^n + a_{n-1}hg^{n-1} + \ldots + a_o h^n = 0,$$

so that $g^n = bh$ with $b \in R$. Assuming that g and h have no common factor, let p be a prime factor of h. Then pR is a prime ideal of R, $g^n \in pR$ but $g \notin pR$ which is impossible.

Let K be a field and let L be a finite extension of K. Let $f_1,\ldots,f_n$ be a basis of L over K. Let $u_1,\ldots,u_n$ be the $n = [L:K]$ distinct K-isomorphisms of L into a fixed algebraic closure $\overline{K}$ of K. Let $d(f_1,\ldots,f_n) = (\det(u_i(f_j)))^2$ be the discriminant of the given basis. If $g_1,\ldots,g_n$ is another basis of L over K and $g_p = \sum a_{pj}f_j$, then $d(g_1,\ldots,g_n) = (\det(a_{pj}))^2 \cdot d(f_1,\ldots,f_n)$, as one can readily verify.

Another way to write the discriminant is given by $d(f_1,\ldots,f_n) = \det(\mathrm{Tr}_{L/K}(f_i f_j))$. If f is a primitive element of L over K, i.e., $L = K(f)$, then $1, f, f^2, \ldots, f^{n-1}$ is a basis of L over K. If we set $f_{(i)} = u_i(f)$, then $d(1,f,f^2,\ldots,f^{n-1}) = \det(f^j_{(i)})$. Since the $f_{(i)}$ are distinct, the Vandermonde determinant is not zero. This shows that if L is separable over K, the bilinear form $\mathrm{Tr}_{L/K}(fg)$ is non-degenerate.

THEOREM 5.48. Let R be a normal noetherian domain with fraction field K. If L is a finite separable extension of K, then the integral closure R' of R in L is a finitely generated R-module.

Proof: First assume that L is a separable galois extension of K. If $f \in L$, then there is an $a \in R$ such that $af \in R'$, for if $f^n + b_{n-1}f^{n-1} + \ldots + b_o = 0$ is the monic minimal equation for f over K, and a is a common denominator in R for the b_i, then $(af)^n + ab_{n-1}(af)^{n-1} + \ldots + a^n b_o = 0$. Thus we can find a basis $g_1,\ldots,g_n$ for L over K with $g_i \in R'$. Let $h_1,\ldots,h_n$ be the dual basis with respect to the non-degenerate bilinear form $\mathrm{Tr}_{L/K}(fg)$. If $f = \sum a_i h_i \in R'$, then $fg_i \in R'$, $1 \leqslant i \leqslant n$, so $\mathrm{Tr}_{L/K}(fg_i) \in R$, as $R = (R')^G$, G being the galois group of L over K. But

$$\mathrm{Tr}_{L/K}(fg_i) = \sum_j a_j \mathrm{Tr}_{L/K}(g_i h_j) = \sum a_i ,$$

so that $R' \subset \sum Rh_j$. Since the latter is a finitely generated R-module, and the integral closure of R in a subfield of L is an R-subalgebra of R', the theorem follows.

COROLLARY 5.49. Let $R = k[x_1,\dots,x_n]$ be a domain with fraction field K. Let L be a finite extension of K and let R' be the integral closure of R in L. Then R' is a finitely generated R-module.

Proof: By 5.44, we may assume that R is a polynomial ring, and hence normal, by 5.46. Let L_o be the separable closure of K in L. By theorem 5.48, the integral closure of R in L_o is a finitely generated R-module. Thus we may assume that L is purely inseparable over K. The same argument as in the proof of theorem 2.26 takes care of this case.

V-7 FINITE GROUPS

THEOREM 5.50. Let R be a finitely generated k-algebra and let G be a finite group of k-algebra automorphisms of R. Then R^G is a finitely generated k-algebra.

Proof: If $R = k[f_1,\dots,f_n]$, then $F_i(X) = \prod_{x \in G} (X - f$

is a monic polynomial with coefficients in the ring R

Also, $F_i(f_i) = 0$. If $F_i(X) = \sum a_{ij}X^j$, $a_{ij} \in R^G$, let $R_o = k[a_{ij}]$. Then R_o is a finitely generated k-algebra and each f_i is integral over R_o. Therefore, R is a finitely generated R_o-module, and so R^G is also a finitely generated R_o-module. Thus R^G is a finitely generated k-algebra.

LEMMA 5.51. Let S be an overring of the ring R which is a finitely generated R-module. If $\underline{m}$ is a maximal ideal of R, then there exists a maximal ideal $\underline{n}$ of S such that $\underline{m} = \underline{n} \cap R$.

Proof: Immediate by localizing at $R - \underline{m}$ and applying 3.9.

The next theorem gives a complete solution to the quotient problem for finite groups

THEOREM 5.52. Let V be an affine algebraic set and let G be a finite group. If G acts on V over k, then a strict quotient of V by G exists and is an affine algebraic set.

Proof: Using the same arguments as in the proof of theorem 5.8, it suffices to establish the following facts. If V_o is an affine model of $k[V]^G$ and $\varphi : V \to V_o$ is the k-morphism induced by the inclusion, then

i) φ is a closed mapping,

ii) If W and W' are two closed disjoint G-invariant subsets of V, then there exists an $f \in k[V_o]$ such that $f|W = 1$ and $f|W' = 0$.

Note that since G is a finite group, the orbits of G in V are finite sets of points and hence closed. Now i) is an immediate consequence of lemma 5.51, since $k[V]$ is a finitely generated $k[V_o]$-module. To see this, let Z be closed in V and let $Z' = \varphi Z$. Then $k[V]/\underline{I}_{V_o}(Z')k[V]$ is a finitely generated $k[V_o]/\underline{I}_{V_o}(Z')$-module, and $\underline{V}_V(\underline{I}_{V_o}(Z')) = Z$. Applying lemma 5.51, we see that Z is mapped onto $\overline{Z'}$.

For ii), note that we can always find an element $g \in k[V]$ such that $g|W = 1$ and $g|W' = 0$. If we set $f = \prod_{x \in G} g^x$, then f has the required properties.

EXERCISE. Describe explicitly the n-th symmetric powe[r] of $\underline{A}^2$, i.e., give a set of polynomials defining it as a closed set in some affine space.

V-8 SEMI-REDUCTIVE GROUPS

In this section, we introduce a notion which is weaker than linear reductivity for affine groups. Thi[s] property is strong enough, however, to ensure finite generation of rings of invariants.

DEFINITION 5.53. Let G be an affine group. G is said to be <u>semi-reductive</u> if the following condition is satisfied. Given a finite dimensional rational G-module M and a G-submodule N such that $\dim N = \dim M - 1$ and G acts trivially on M/N, there is an integer n and an $f \in (S^n M)^G$ with $f \notin N \cdot S^{n-1} M$.

EXERCISE. Show that a finite group is semi-reductive.

Throughout this section, G is a semi-reductive affine group acting rationally by k-algebra automorphisms on the k-algebra R.

LEMMA 5.54. If I is a G-invariant ideal of R, then for each $f \in (R/I)^G$, there is an integer t such that $f^t \in R^G/I \cap R^G$.

<u>Proof</u>: Choose a g in R whose image in R/I is f. Let M be the subspace of R generated by the translates of g and let $N = M \cap I$. Assume $f \neq 0$. Then $g^x - g \in N$ for all $x \in G$. Thus if $M' = kg + N$, there is a G-invariant $F \in S^t M'$, for a suitable t such that F is monic in g. If f_o is the image of F in R under the canonical homomorphism $S(M') \to R$, then $f_o \in R^G$ and the image of f_o in R/I is f^t.

LEMMA 5.55. If $f_1, \ldots, f_s \in R^G$ then every element of $(\sum f_i R) \cap R^G$ is nilpotent modulo $\sum f_i R^G$.

<u>Proof</u>: We use induction on s. Let $I_j = \sum_{i=1}^{j} f_i R$. Let $\overline{R} = R/f_1 R$ and let f be an element of $I_s \cap R^G$. Then $\overline{f} \in \overline{I}_s \cap \overline{R^G}$. But $\overline{I}_s = \sum_{i=2}^{s} \overline{f}_i \overline{R}$. By induction, it follows that there is an integer t with $\overline{f}^t \in \sum_{i=1}^{s} \overline{f}_i \overline{R}^G$. Therefore $f^t = \sum_{i=1}^{s} f_i g_i$ where $g_1 \in R$ and $\overline{g}_2, \ldots, \overline{g}_s \in \overline{R}^G$. By lemma 5.54, there is an integer u such that $\overline{g}_s^u \in \overline{R^G}$. Replacing f^t by f^{tu}, we may assume that $g_s \in R^G$. If $s > 1$, then $f^t - f_s g_s \in I_{s-1} \cap R^G$ and is nilpotent modulo $\sum_{i=1}^{s-1} f_i R^G$. If $s = 1$, then $f = f_1 g$ for some $g \in R$ and g must be invariant modulo the ideal $(0:f_1) = \{h \in R : hf_1 = 0$ Let $R' = R/(0:f_1)$. Then $g' \in (R')^G$ so that $g'^t \in (R^G)'$ for some t. If h is an element of R^G with $h' = (g^t)'$, then $f^t = f_1^t g^t = f_1^t h \in f_1 R^G$.

The following theorem is due to Nagata, and is the most general result available at present on finite generation of rings of invariants.

THEOREM 5.56. Let G be a semi-reductive affine group acting rationally on the finitely generated k-algebra R by k-algebra automorphisms. Then R^G is finitely generated.

Proof: Since R is a finitely generated k-algebra, there is a polynomial ring $S = k[X_1,\ldots,X_n]$ with $R = S/Q$ for some ideal Q in S. First we assume that R is graded and G acts homogeneously on R. Then Q is homogeneous and S may be chosen so that it is a rational G-module and the canonical surjection $S \twoheadrightarrow R$ is a homomorphism of G-modules, e.g., take $S = S(M)$ where M is a finite dimensional G-submodule of R containing a set of generators for R over k.

By noetherian induction, we may also assume that if $Q' > Q$ is a G-invariant homogeneous ideal of S then $(S/Q')^G$ is finitely generated. Thus if $J \neq (0)$ is a G-invariant homogeneous ideal of R, then we may write $(R/J)^G = k[f_1,\ldots,f_t]$. By lemma 5.54, $(R/J)^G$ is integral over the ring $R^G/J \cap R^G$. If R_o is the subring of $R^G/J \cap R^G$ generated by the coefficients of suitable integral dependence relations for the f_i, then - as in 5.50 - $(R/J)^G$ is a finitely generated R_o-module, whence $R^G/J \cap R^G$ is also. Thus $R^G/J \cap R^G$ is a finitely generated k-algebra.

If we can find a J as above so that $J \cap R^G$ has a finite ideal basis, then we can apply lemma 5.7 to the graded ring R^G by noting that if $g_1,\ldots,g_m$ is a basis of $(R^G/J \cap R^G)_+$, $h_1,\ldots,h_m$ are representatives in R^G for the g_i and $u_1,\ldots,u_p$ is a basis for $J \cap R^G$, then $h_1,\ldots,h_m,u_1,\ldots,u_p$ is a basis for $(R^G)_+$.

If $f \in R^G$ is a homogeneous non-zero-divisor of positive degree in R, then $fR \cap R^G = fR^G$ and we can take $J = fR$. In general, let f be homogeneous of positive degree and let $I = (0:f)$. If $I \neq (0)$ then by induction, we may assume that the rings $R^G/fR \cap R^G$ and $R^G/I \cap R^G$ are finitely generated. Notice that I is homogeneous since f is. If $F_1,\ldots,F_r$ generate R^G modulo $fR \cap R^G$ and $G_1,\ldots,G_s$ generate R^G modulo $I \cap R^G$, let $R_1 = k[F_1,\ldots,F_r,G_1,\ldots,G_s]$. Then $R_1 \subset R^G$ and R_1 maps onto both of the rings $R^G/fR \cap R^G$ and $R^G/I \cap R^G$. Since $(R/I)^G$ is a finitely generated $(R_1/I \cap R_1)$-module, we can find elements $c_1,\ldots,c_t$ of R whose residues modulo I generate this module over $R_1/I \cap$ Since c_i is G-invariant modulo I, it follows that $c_i f$ is G-invariant. If $g \in R^G$, choose an $h \in R_1$ so that $g - h \in fR$, i.e., $g - h = fr$ for some $r \in R$. Then $fr \in R^G$ and so fr is G-invariant modulo I. Thus there is an element b in the module $\sum R_1 c$ such that $r - b \in I$. This implies that $fr = fb \in R_1[fc_1,\ldots,fc_t]$. Therefore $R^G = R_1[fc_1,\ldots,fc_t]$.

In case Q is not homogeneous, the induction carries over - taking $f \in R^G$, the above argument applies if f is a zero-divisor. Thus we need only consider the case where no non-zero element of R^G is a zero-divisor in R. In particular R^G is a domain. Moreover, S^G is finitely generated by the homogeneous case, and R^G is integral over $S^G/Q \cap S^G$.

Assume now that the fraction field K of R^G is a finitely generated extension of k. Then K is algebraic over the fraction field K_o of $S^G/Q \cap S^G$. Hence K is a finite extension of K_o. Therefore, by corollary 5.49, R^G is a finitely generated module over $S^G/Q \cap S^G$, and hence a finitely generated k-algebra.

It remains only to show that K is a finitely generated extension of k. Let T be the multiplicative set of non-zero-divisors in R. Then $\varphi_T : R \to T^{-1}R$ is injective. Let $\underline{m}$ be a maximal ideal of $T^{-1}R$. Then $\underline{m} \cap R^G = (0)$, so it suffices, by lemma 2.25, to show that the field $T^{-1}R/\underline{m}$ is a finitely generated extension of k. But $T^{-1}R/\underline{m}$ is just the fraction field of $R/\underline{m} \cap R$ and the latter is a finitely generated k-algebra. q.e.d.

REMARK. The assertion that a reductive affine group is semi-reductive is known as "Mumford's conjecture". Actually, as we have seen, the conjecture is uninteresting in characteristic zero, since a reductive affine group is linearly reductive and *a fortiori* semi-reductive. Now one has the following

LEMMA 5.57. Let G be an affine group and N be a closed normal subgroup of G. If N and G/N are semi-reductive, then G is semi-reductive.

Proof: Let M be a finite dimensional rational G-module and let M' be a G-invariant hyperplane in M such that G acts trivially on M/M'. Choose an integer n and an $f \in (S^n M)^N$ with $f \notin M'S^{n-1}M$. Let P be the G-submodule of $S(M)$ generated by the element f. Then P is a finite dimensional rational G/N-module, since N must act trivially on P. Let $P' = M'S(M) \cap P$. Then P' is a G-invariant hyperplane in P such that G acts trivially on P/P'. Thus we can find an integer m and a $g \in (S^m P)^G = (S^m P)^{G/N}$ such that $g \notin P'S^{m-1}P$. Then the image of g under the canonical mapping $S(P) \rightarrow S(M)$ lies in $(S^{nm}M)^G$ but not in $M'S^{nm-1}M$.

This means that the only case of Mumford's conjecture to be considered is that of a semisimple affine group in characteristic $p > 0$. In this situation, the conjecture has been verified by Seshadri for SL_2 and this is the only positive evidence for the conjecture. Seshadri's proof runs as follows.

First of all, note that semi-reductivity for an affine group G is equivalent to the following condition. If $G \subset GL_r$ and L is a G-invariant 1-dimensional linear subspace of $\underline{A}^r$, then there exists a G-invariant homogeneous hypercone C in $\underline{A}^r$ not containing L.

Next, we note that if this condition holds for

a given rational G-module, then it holds for any G-submodule.

Finally, we observe that if the condition holds for two rational G-modules M_1 and M_2, then it holds for the rational G-module $M_1 \times M_2$. For if L is an invariant line in $M_1 \times M_2$ then the projection of L in both factors cannot be (0) and must be invariant. Thus if L projects to $(0) \neq L_1 \subset M_1$ and if C_1 is a homogeneous G-invariant hypercone in M_1 not containing L_1, then $C_1 \times M_2$ is a homogeneous G-invariant hypercone in $M_1 \times M_2$ not containing L.

Recall that if M is a finite dimensional rational GL_r-module, then M is isomorphic to a submodule of $k[GL_r]^n$ for some n. Multiplying by a suitable power of the determinant, we may assume that M is a submodule of $k[\underline{A}^{r^2}]^n$. As $k[\underline{A}^{r^2}] = k[\underline{A}^r] \otimes \cdots \otimes k[\underline{A}^r]$, ($r$ factors), we may assume that M has the form $S^{p_1}V \otimes \cdots \otimes S^{p_r}V$, where $V = \underline{A}^r$ with the standard action of GL_r.

The only semi-invariants of GL_r in $k[\underline{A}^{r^2}]$ are of the form aD^m where D is the determinant. This is easily seen from the fact that the locus of the determinant is the complement of GL_r in $M_r(k) = \underline{A}^{r^2}$.

Now we consider the case $r = 2$. Note that

$$(XY - UV)^m = \sum_{p=0}^{m} (-1)^p \binom{m}{p} (XY)^{m-p} (UV)^p$$

$$= \sum_{p=0}^{m} (-1)^p \binom{m}{p} (X^{m-p}U^p)(Y^{m-p}V^p) \quad ,$$

so that D^m can be considered as an element of $S^mV \otimes S^mV$, $V = \underline{A}^2$. The key point in the proof is the exactness of the sequence

$$0 \rightarrow S^{m-1}V \otimes S^{m-1}V \xrightarrow{v} S^mV \otimes S^mV \xrightarrow{u} S^{2m}V \rightarrow 0 ,$$

where $u(f \otimes g) = fg$ and

$$v(X^{m-j-1}Y^j \otimes X^{m-p-1}Y^p) =$$

$$X^{m-j}Y^j \otimes X^{m-p}Y^p - X^{m-j-1}Y^{j+1} \otimes X^{m-p-1}Y^{p+1} .$$

Since every form in two variables over an algebraicall closed field can be written as a product of linear forms, it follows that u is surjective. A simple dimension count shows the sequence is exact.

Now if T is the set of reducible tensors in $S^mV \otimes S^mV$, then $u^{-1}(s) \cap T$ is finite for all $s \in S^{2}$ T is evidently a GL_2-invariant homogeneous cone in $S^mV \otimes S^mV$. Now we apply induction to find a GL_2-invariant homogeneous hypercone T' in $S^{m-1}V \otimes S^{m-1}V$ not containing D^{m-1}. The linear join of T and T' is then a GL_2-invariant homogeneous hypercone in $S^mV \otimes S^mV$. Since $v(D^{m-1}) = D^m$ and since $T \cap \ker u = (0)$, we see that D^m does not lie in this join. Therefore SL_2 is semi-reductive.

V-9 THE NORMALIZATION OF AN AFFINE VARIETY

For many purposes it is convenient when studying an affine variety to know that its coordinate ring is normal. This is not always the case as one sees from the curve $X^3 - Y^2 = 0$ in $\underline{A}^2$. The coordinate ring here is isomorphic to the subring $k[t^2,t^3]$ of $k[t]$, t a variable. t is integral over this ring but is not in it.

There is a canonical way to associate to any affine variety V a "normal" affine variety V' and a surjective k-morphism $\pi : V' \to V$ such that $k(V) = k(V')$.

DEFINITION 5.58. Let V be an affine variety. Let $k[V]'$ be the integral closure of $k[V]$ in $k(V)$. An affine model of $k[V]'$ is called a <u>normalization</u> of V in $k(V)$. Since any two normalizations of V in $k(V)$ are k-isomorphic, we will speak of the normalization of V in $k(V)$. Note that corollary 5.49 guarantees that $k[V]'$ is an affine algebra.

PROPOSITION 5.59. Let V be an affine variety and let V' be its normalization. Let $\pi: V' \to V$ be the k-morphism induced by the inclusion $k[V] \subset k[V'] = k[V]'$. Then π is surjective, and for each $v \in V$, $\pi^{-1}(v)$ is a finite set of points.

<u>Proof</u>: Let $R = k[V]$, $R' = k[V']$. Then R' is a finitely generated R-module. If $\underline{m}$ is a maximal ideal of R, let $T = R - \underline{m}$. Then $T^{-1}R = R_{\underline{m}}$ is the local ring of the point corresponding to $\underline{m}$ on V and $T^{-1}R'$ is a finitely generated $R_{\underline{m}}$-module. By

Nakayama's lemma, $\underline{m}(T^{-1}R') \neq T^{-1}R'$, so π is surjective. If $v \in V$ corresponds to $\underline{m}$, the points of $\pi^{-1}(v)$ are in bijective correspondence with the maximal ideals of $T^{-1}R'$. To see this, let $\underline{n}$ be a maximal ideal of $T^{-1}R'$. Then $\underline{n} \cap R = \underline{m}$ and $R'/\underline{m}R'$ is a finitely generated $R/\underline{m}$-module. Since $\underline{m}R' \subset \underline{n} \cap R'$ and the latter must be a prime ideal of R', it follows that $R'/\underline{n} \cap R' = k$. Hence $\underline{n} \cap R'$ is a maximal ideal of R'. However, $\underline{n} = (\underline{n} \cap R')T^{-1}R$

The ring $R_o = (T^{-1}R')/\underline{m}(T^{-1}R')$ is a finite dimensional k-algebra, so that $U(R_o)$ is a Zariski open set in R_o. Its complement is then a finite union of proper subvarieties of R_o. Since any maximal ideal in R_o is a hyperplane in R_o, there can only be a finite number of maximal ideals.

EXERCISE. Show that there is a non-empty open set U in V' which is mapped isomorphically by π to an open set U in V.

DEFINITION 5.60. We say that an affine variety is normal if its coordinate ring is normal.

DEFINITION 5.61. Let V be an affine variety and let v be a point of V. We say that $f \in k(V)$ is defined at v if $f \in \underline{o}_{V,v}$. In this case, we denote by f(v) the residue of f modulo $\underline{m}_v$. We say that f is infinite at v if $1/f \in \underline{m}_v$.

It can happen that an element of $k(V)$ is neither defined nor infinite at a point of V. For example, let $V = \underline{A}^2$, $v = (0,0)$ and $f = Y/X$.

Now let V be an affine variety and let $f \in k(V)$. Then the inclusion $k[V] \subset k[V][f]$ induces a k-morphism $\varphi : W \to V$ where W is an affine model of $k[V][f]$. We say that f is definable at $v \in V$ if $\varphi^{-1}(v)$ consists of a single point. This point having coordinates (v, v_o) in $V \times \underline{A}^1$, we write $v_o = f(v)$.

PROPOSITION 5.62. Let V be a normal affine variety, v a point of V, and $f \in k(V)$. If f is definable at v, then f is defined at v.

Proof: Let $g = 1/f$. (If $f = 0$, there is nothing to prove.) If g is definable at v, then evidently $f(v) \neq 0 \neq g(v)$. On the other hand, it is clear that either g is definable at v or $f(v) = 0$. Thus in neither case can we have $g(v) = 0$. Now if $k[V] = k[f_1,\ldots,f_r]$, then there is a polynomial $F(X_1,\ldots,X_r,X)$ such that $F(f_1,\ldots,f_r,f) = 0$, $F(f_1(v),\ldots,f_r(v),0) \neq 0$. Let $F = \sum G_i X^i$. Then $G_o(f_1(v),\ldots,f_r(v)) \neq 0$. Setting $h_i = G_i(f_1,\ldots,f_r)/G_o(f_1,\ldots,f_r)$, we note that $h_i \in \underline{o}_{V,v}$. But then $1 + h_1 g + \ldots + h_n g^n = 0$ so that $f^n + h_1 f^{n-1} + \ldots + h_n = 0$, and therefore f is integral over $\underline{o}_{V,v}$. To complete the proof, it suffices to show that $\underline{o}_{V,v}$ is normal. This follows from:

LEMMA 5.63. Let R be a normal domain and let T be a multiplicative set in R with $0 \notin T$. Then $T^{-1}R$ is a normal domain.

<u>Proof</u>: If f is in the fraction field of R and $f^n + a_{n-1}f^{n-1} + \dots + a_o = 0$, with $a_i \in T^{-1}R$, let $t \in T$ be a common denominator for the a_i. Then $(tf)^n + ta_{n-1}(tf)^{n-1} + \dots + t^n a_o = 0$, whence tf is integral over R. Therefore $tf \in R$, i.e., $f \in T^{-1}R$.

PROPOSITION 5.64. Let V be an affine variety. If $f \in k(V)$ is definable at $v \in V$, then f is integral over $\underline{o}_{V,v}$.

<u>Proof</u>: If $\pi : V' \to V$ is the normalization of V in $k(V)$, then the hypothesis implies that f is definable at each point of $\pi^{-1}(v)$, so by 5.62,

$$f \in \bigcap_{v' \in \pi^{-1}(v)} \underline{o}_{V',v'} .$$

Let $R = k[V]$, $R' = k[V']$. Then $R' \otimes_R \underline{o}_{V,v}$ is a finitely generated $\underline{o}_{V,v}$-module because R' is a finitely generated R-module. Denoting the tensor product by S, it suffices to show that S is equal to the above intersection. If $v_1', \dots, v_r'$ are the points of $\pi^{-1}(v)$, then the maximal ideals of S are of the form $\underline{m}_i'S$ where $\underline{m}_i'$ is the maximal ideal in R' corresponding to v_i'. Thus if T_i' is the multiplicative set $S - \underline{m}_i'S$, then $\underline{o}_{V',v_i'} = (T_i')^{-1}S$.

The proposition now follows from

LEMMA 5.65. Let R be a domain. Then $R = \bigcap R_{\underline{m}}$, the intersection being taken over all maximal ideals of R.

Proof: Since the reverse inclusion is obvious, we prove that $\bigcap R_{\underline{m}} \subset R$. If $g, h \in R$ and $g/h \in \bigcap R_{\underline{m}}$ then $g \in hR_{\underline{m}}$ for all $\underline{m}$. Therefore, for each $\underline{m}$ there is an $f_{\underline{m}} \in R - \underline{m}$ such that $f_{\underline{m}} g \in hR$. Thus the ideal $(hR:gR) = \{f \in R : fgR \subset hR\}$ is contained in no $\underline{m}$, i.e., $(hR:gR) = R$ and $g \in hR$ as required.

EXERCISE. Let V be an irreducible affine curve, i.e., a 1-dimensional affine variety. If V' is the normalization of V, show that V' is smooth at each of its points.

V-10 WEITZENBOCK'S THEOREM

In this section we give Seshadri's proof of Weitzenbock's result on 1-dimensional affine groups referred to in section 1. The characteristic is zero.

LEMMA 5.66. Let G be a connected affine group and let H be a closed subgroup of G. Let V be an affine variety and let $\alpha : G \times V \to V$ be an action of G on V over k. Let W be an H-stable subvariety of V and assume that for all $v \in W$, $o_H(v) = o_G(v) \cap W$. Let $X = \alpha(G \times W)$. If $f \in k[W]^H$ then there exists an element $g \in k(\overline{X})^G$ such that g is definable at each point of X and $g|W = f$.

Proof: Clearly we may assume that $V = \overline{X}$. Suppose we have $xv = x'v'$ for $x, x' \in G$, $v, v' \in W$. Then $x'^{-1}xv = v' = yv$ for some $y \in H$. Thus $f(v') = f(yv) = f(v)$. If p_2 is the projection of $G \times W$ on W and $F = p_2(f)$, then F is constant on each fibre $\alpha^{-1}(v)$, $v \in X$. Let Z be an affine model of $k[V]$. Then the induced morphism of Z into V is bijective over X. But as X contains a non-empty open subset of V, it follows that $k(V) = k(Z)$ since the characteristic is zero. Letting g denote the element of $k(V)$ induced by F, we see that g is G-invariant by definition, that g is definable at each $v \in X$, viz., $g(v) = f(v)$, and that $g|W = f$.

THEOREM 5.67. Let G be a 1-dimensional closed subgroup of GL_n. If k has characteristic zero, then $k[\underline{A}^n]^G$ is finitely generated.

Proof: By 5.50, we may assume that G is connected. Thus either $G = G_u$ or $G = G_s$. In the latter case, the theorem holds in any characteristic, so we assume that $G = G_u$. Since the characteristic is zero, this means that G is isomorphic to G_a.

We regard G_a as a closed subgroup of SL_2 via

the representation, $t \mapsto \begin{pmatrix} 1 & t \\ 0 & 1 \end{pmatrix}$. We want to extend the given representation $\rho : G_a \to GL_n$ to a representation $\rho^*: SL_2 \to GL_n$. This is the essential part of Weitzenbock's original proof, although it appears there in a very "classical" guise.

To see that the extension is possible, let $t \in G_a$ and assume that $t \neq 0$. Since the closure of the subgroup generated by t is G_a itself, it suffices to deal with t alone. Let the Jordan normal form of $\rho(t)$ be

$$\begin{pmatrix} A_1 & & & 0 \\ & A_2 & & \\ & & \ddots & \\ 0 & & & A_r \end{pmatrix}$$

where

$$A_i = \begin{pmatrix} 1 & 1 & 0 & \dots & 0 \\ 0 & 1 & 1 & 0 . & 0 \\ & & \dots & & \\ & & & 1 & 1 \\ & & & & 1 \end{pmatrix}$$

If A_i has degree d_i, let ρ_i^* be the representation of SL_2 on $S^{d_i-1}\underline{A}^2$ induced by the standard representation of SL_2 on $\underline{A}^2$. If, e.g., we take $t = 1$, the Jordan normal form of $\rho_i^*(t)$ is A_i - simply look at $S^{d_i-1}\begin{pmatrix} 1 & 1 \\ 0 & 1 \end{pmatrix}$. If we order the monomials of degree d in X and Y by decreasing powers of X, viz., $X^d, X^{d-1}Y, X^{d-2}Y^2, \dots, X^2Y^{d-2}, XY^{d-1}, Y^d$, then $X^{d-j}Y^j$ is mapped to $(X + Y)^{d-j}Y^j = X^{d-j}Y^j + (d-j)X^{d-j-1}Y^{j+1} + \dots + Y^d$ and it is clear how to proceed.

Of course, we can get this normal form for any fixed $t \neq 0$. Then we set

$$\rho^*(t) = \begin{pmatrix} \rho_1^*(t) & & \\ & \ddots & \\ & & \rho_r^*(t) \end{pmatrix}, \quad t \in G_a.$$

Since any non-trivial representation of G_a in characteristic zero is faithful, ρ^* is faithful. Now in lemma 5.66, we take G to be the closed subgroup of GL_{n+2} given by the matrices

$$(1) \qquad \begin{pmatrix} \rho^*(x) & 0 \\ 0 & x \end{pmatrix} \quad , \quad x \in SL_2 \; ,$$

and H to be the subgroup:

$$\begin{pmatrix} \rho^*(t) & 0 \\ 0 & \begin{pmatrix} 1 & t \\ 0 & 1 \end{pmatrix} \end{pmatrix} \quad , \quad t \in G_a.$$

Then G acts on $k[\underline{A}^{n+2}] = k[X_1,\ldots,X_n,X_{n+1},X_{n+2}]$ If $V = \underline{A}^{n+2}$ and W is the locus of $(X_{n+1},X_{n+2} - 1)$ then W is H-stable. Now for $x \in SL_2$, let x' denote the matrix (1) above. If $x'(x_1,\ldots,x_n,0,1) = (x_1',\ldots,x_n',0,1)$, then $x(0,1) = (0,1)$, so that $x \in G_a$. This shows that the orbit condition of 5.66 is satisfied. Using the notation of that lemma, we see that X contains the complement of the locus of $(X_{n+}$ $X_{n+2})$, so that $V = \overline{X}$.

Now each of the rational functions on V given by 5.66 is integral over the local rings of points of X

But as V is normal, these functions lie in these rings. In fact, since $V = \underline{A}^{n+2}$, they all lie in $k[V]$, (cf. the exercise below). As SL_2 is semi-simple, $k[V]^{SL_2}$ is finitely generated. By 5.66, it follows that $k[W]^{G_a}$ is a homomorphic image of this ring.

EXERCISE. Show that a rational function on $\underline{A}^n$, defined at all points of $\underline{A}^n$ except possibly those on a closed subset of dimension $\leq n - 2$, is actually a polynomial.

V-11 FISCHER'S THEOREM

THEOREM 5.68. Let $k = \mathbf{C}$ and let G be a closed subgroup of GL_n such that x G implies ${}^t\bar{x}$ G, where $\bar{x}$ denotes the complex conjugate of x. Then G is reductive.

Proof: Since R(G) is invariant under all continuous automorphisms of G, we see that x $({}^t\bar{x})^{-1}$ takes R(G) to R(G). If x is a unipotent element of R(G), then so is $({}^t\bar{x})^{-1}$ and so ${}^t\bar{x}x$ is hermitean. But a hermitean matrix is diagonalizable, so ${}^t\bar{x}x = 1$. This means that x is unitary, and a unitary matrix is diagonalizable, so x = 1. Thus $R(G)_u = (1)$.

MISCELLANEOUS EXERCISES

CHAPTER I

1. Show that any affine algebraic set is quasi-compact in the Zariski topology. If $k = \mathbf{C}$, show that an affine algebraic set is compact in the complex topology if and only if it is finite. (Recall that the complex topology is the one inherited from the product topology on $\underline{A}^n = \mathbf{C}^n$.)

2. Let V be a (Zariski) closed subset of $\mathbf{C}^n$. Show that V is closed in the complex topology. Show that V is connected in the Zariski topology if and only if it is connected in the complex topology.

3. Let V be an affine algebraic set. Show that V is connected if and only if $k[V]$ is not a direct sum of two non-zero ideals.

4. Let K be a finitely generated extension field of k of transcendence degree 1. Show that any subring of K containing k is noetherian. We have already seen that this is false for extensions of higher transcendence degree.

5. Let F and G be irreducible polynomials in k[X,Y]. If F does not divide G show that the locus of (F,G) in $\underline{A}^2$ is a finite set of points.

6. Let V be a Zariski closed subset of $\underline{A}^n$. Show that the following are also closed in the Zariski topology.

i) the cone over V with vertex p.

ii) any linear projection of V into a linear variety in $\underline{A}^n$.

iii) the tangent locus of V, i.e., the union of the $T_v(V)$, $v \in V$.

7. By an algebra over k we mean a vector space A over k plus an element of $A_{1,2}$. Show that if A is finite dimensional, then the set of $u \in A_{1,2}$ such that the corresponding algebra has each of the following properties is closed in the Zariski topology on $A_{1,2}$.

i) A is an associative algebra.

ii) A is a Lie algebra.

iii) A is a nil algebra, i.e., every element of A is nilpotent.

iv) A is a commutative algebra.

8. Show that an affine algebraic set is Hausdorff in the Zariski topology if and only if it is finite.

CHAPTER II

1. Let G be an affine group and let H be a subgroup of G. Show that $\overline{H}$ is a subgroup of G. If X is a subset of G, show that the centralizer of X is a closed subgroup of G. If X is closed in G, show that its normalizer is a closed subgroup of G.

2. Show that the only k-homomorphisms of GL_n into G_m are powers of the determinant, viz., $\widehat{GL_n} = \mathbf{Z}$.

3. Let G be an affine group. A maximal torus in G is called a Cartan subgroup of G and a maximal connected solvable subgroup of G is called a Borel subgroup of G. Determine all Cartan subgroups and all Borel subgroups of GL_n, SL_n, O_n, and Sp_n.

4. Show that $k[GL_n]$ is a unique factorization domain and that $k[PGL_n]$ is not a unique factorization domain unless $n = 0$. Show that $k[SL_n]$ is a unique factorization domain.

5. Let GL_n act on $S^p\underline{A}^n$ via the representation induced by the standard action on $\underline{A}^n$. Show that there are always non-closed orbits for this action.

6. Let n be a fixed non-negative integer. Let $\underline{r} = (n_1,\ldots,n_s)$, $n_1 + \ldots + n_s = n$. Let $GL_{\underline{r}}$ be the closed subgroup of GL_n consisting of matrices

$$\begin{pmatrix} A_1 & & & 0 \\ & A_2 & & \\ & & \ddots & \\ 0 & & & A_s \end{pmatrix}$$

where $A_i \in GL_{n_i}$. Describe the quotient of GL_n by $GL_{\underline{r}}$.

7. Let G_m act on $\underline{A}^n$ by scalar multiplication. Describe $k[\underline{A}^n]^{G_m}$. Does a strict quotient of $\underline{A}^n$ by G_m exist in this case? Does a quotient exist?

8. Let the alternating group A_n act on $\underline{A}^n$ by permuting the coordinates. Describe the quotient of $\underline{A}^n$ by A_n.

9. Let V_o be a strict quotient of the affine algebraic set V by an action of the affine group G. Show that if G and V_o are connected, then V is connected. Show that if G is connected and V_o is a variety, then V is a variety.

10. Show that a connected affine group is a normal variety. (One elegant global way to do this is to show that the normalization of G is itself an

affine group and that the canonical morphism π: $G' \to G$ is a k-homomorphism. The essential trick here is to show that $G' \times G'$ is the normalization of $G \times G$.)

CHAPTER III

1. Let R and S be k-algebras and let $\mathrm{Alg}_k(R,S)$ denote the set of k-algebra homomorphisms from R into S. Show that there is a canonical bijection from $\mathrm{Alg}_k(R_1 \otimes_k R_2, S)$ to $\mathrm{Alg}_k(R_1,S) \times \mathrm{Alg}_k(R_2,S)$.

If G is an affine group over k and R is a commutative k-algebra with identity, let $G(R) = \mathrm{Alg}_k(k[G],R)$. Show that the Hopf structure on $k[G]$ makes $G(R)$ into a group in such a way that if $\varphi: R \to R'$ is a homomorphism of k-algebras, then $G(R) \to G(R')$ is a homomorphism of groups. Show that $G(k)$ can be identified with the set of points of G.

2. Let M be a finite dimensional vector space over k and let $k_M = S(M)/\sum_{i \geq 2} S^i M$. Show that $k_{M \oplus N}$ is canonically isomorphic to $k_M \otimes_k k_N$. Let R be a commutative k-algebra with identity and let $\underline{m}$ be a fixed maximal ideal of R. Denote by $\mathrm{Alg}_{k,\underline{m}}(R,k_M)$ the set of all $f \in \mathrm{Alg}_k(R,k_M)$ such that $f^{-1}M = \underline{m}$. Show that there is a canonical

bijection

$$\mathrm{Alg}_{k,\underline{m}}(R, k_M \otimes_k k_N) \qquad \mathrm{Alg}_{k,\underline{m}}(R, k_M) \times \mathrm{Alg}_{k,\underline{m}}(R, k_N).$$

Use this to define a k-vector space structure on $\mathrm{Alg}_{k,\underline{m}}(R, k_M)$ via the map

$$\mathrm{Alg}_{k,\underline{m}}(R, k_M \otimes_k k_M) \to \mathrm{Alg}_{k,\underline{m}}(R, k_M)$$

coming from the algebra structure on k_M.

Show that if $R = k[V]$ for some affine algebraic set V and if the maximal ideal $\underline{m}$ corresponds to the point $v \in V$, then the vector space $\mathrm{Alg}_{k,\underline{m}}(k[V], k_k)$ is canonically isomorphic to $T_v(V)$.

3. Let $L(G)$ be the kernel of the homomorphism $G(k_k) \to G(k)$ induced by the augmentation $k_k \to k$. Using exercise 2, show that $L(G)$ has a natural structure of vector space over k. Given X, Y $L(G)$, we define $[X,Y]$ to be the composite

$$k[G] \xrightarrow{\tilde{m}} k[G] \otimes_k k[G] \xrightarrow{X \otimes Y - Y \otimes X} k_k \otimes_k k_k \to k_k .$$

Show that with this bracket, $L(G)$ is a Lie algebra over k, canonically isomorphic to $\underline{g}$.

What is the relation between this structure on $L(G)$ and its structure as a subgroup of $G(k_k)$?

4. Let $k = \mathbf{C}$ and let G be a closed subgroup of GL_n (for the Zariski topology). We define a map $\exp : \underline{gl}_n \to GL_n$ by $\exp(X) = \sum_{n=0}^{\infty} X^n/n!$

Show that the series converges uniformly on any bounded region in $\underline{gl}_n$. Show that $\exp \underline{g}$ G. More generally, show that if $f : G \rightarrow G'$ is a $\mathbf{C}$-homomorphism of affine groups, then $\exp(df(X)) = f(\exp(X))$ for any $X \in \underline{g}$. Deduce that if a is a $\mathbf{C}$-automorphism of the connected affine group G, such that $da = 1_{\underline{g}}$ then $a = 1_G$.

CHAPTER IV

1. Show that

$$\dim SL_n = n^2 - 1$$
$$\dim O_n = \tfrac{1}{2}(n^2 - n)$$
$$\dim Sp_n = 2n^2 + n$$
$$\dim PGL_n = n^2 + 2n .$$

2. Let k have characteristic zero. Use lemma 5.19 to show that every semisimple Lie algebra over k is the Lie algebra of a suitable affine group.

3. Let L_1 and L_2 be Lie algebras over k. Show that if M_1 is a simple L_1-module and M_2 is a simple L_2-module, then $M_1 \otimes M_2$ is a simple $L_1 \times L_2$-module. (L_1, L_2, M_1, and M_2 are, of course, finite dimensional.) Show that any simple $L_1 \times L_2$-

module is isomorphic to such a tensor product. Use this to show that $\underline{sl}_n$ is a simple Lie algebra for $n \geqslant 2$. (Hint: count dimensions.)

4. Let k have characteristic zero. Show that $\underline{sl}_4$ acts irreducibly on $\Lambda^2 \underline{A}^4$ in such a way as to leave invariant a suitable non-degenerate quadratic form. Deduce that $\underline{sl}_4$ is isomorphic to $\underline{o}_6$.

5. Show that $\underline{o}_4$ is isomorphic to $\underline{sl}_2 \times \underline{sl}_2$. Note that $\underline{sl}_2 = \underline{sp}_1$ and that if $F = x_1y_2 - x_2y_1$ is the standard skew form on $\underline{A}^2$, then $F \otimes F$ is a symmetric form on $\underline{A}^4$.

CHAPTER V

1. Let V be the affine curve $Y^2 = X^3 - X$ in $\underline{A}^2$. Then $G = \mathbf{Z}/2\mathbf{Z}$ acts on V in a natural way. What is the quotient?

2. Let G be the closed subgroup of O_n consisting of matrices $\begin{pmatrix} A & 0 \\ 0 & 1 \end{pmatrix}$ where $A \in O_{n-1}$. Describe the quotient of O_n by G where the action is the usual one, viz., right translation in O_n.

3. Let M be the space $S^4\underline{A}^2$ and let SL_2 act on M via the natural action on $\underline{A}^2$. Describe the ring $S(M^*)^{SL_2}$. (This is the classical case

of invariants of binary quartics. The actions of SL_2 on $S^p\underline{A}^2$ constitute the theory of 'binary quantics' - in its affine form. The complete story is known only for $p \leqslant 8$. The case $p = 8$ was only recently done by T. Shioda.)

4. Let G be a Borel subgroup of GL_n (cf. ex. 3, ch. II) and let G act by right translation. Show that $k[GL_n]^G = k$. Despite this, one can show that there is a natural identification of the set GL_n/G with the set of flags in $\underline{A}^n$, which can be be made algebraic with the machinery of projective geometry.

5. Show by an example that if G is an affine group and H is a closed subgroup, then if $f \in k[G]$ is right H-invariant, it need not be left H-invariant. Show, however, that there is a k-algebra automorphism of $k[G]$ taking the ring of right invariants onto the ring of left invariants.

6. Show that if G is a connected affine group such that $\hat{G} = (0)$ and G acts by k-algebra automorphisms on the k-algebra R so that R is a rational G-module, then if R is a unique factorization domain, so is R^G. Show that if k has characteristic zero and G is semisimple, then $\hat{G} = (0)$.

7. Let G be a linearly reductive 1-dimensional connected affine group. Show that G is isomorphic to G_m in any characteristic. (Nagata has proved that a linearly reductive connected affine group in characteristic $p > 0$ is necessarily a torus.)

8. Show that the Lie algebra of a unipotent affine group is nilpotent.

9. Let G be an affine group and let H and K be closed connected subgroups of G. Show that if H and K have the same Lie algebra, then $H = K$. Deduce that if a is any k-automorphism of G such that $da = 1_{\underline{g}}$ then $a = 1_G$ if G is connected. (Hint: consider the graph of a in $G \times G$.)

10. Let the affine group G act on the affine algebraic set V. Show that there is at least one closed orbit for the action. Describe the closed orbits for the standard action of GL_n on $S^2\underline{A}^n$ and of O_n on $S^2\underline{A}^n$.

11. Describe the following rings of invariants. In each case, the action of the subgroup is by right translation. $k[GL_n]^{SL_n}$, $k[GL_n]^{O_n}$, $k[GL_{2n}]^{Sp_n}$, $k[SL_n]^{SO_n}$, and $k[SL_{2n}]^{Sp_n}$. ($SO_n = O_n \cap SL_n$).

12. Show that every k-automorphism of the affine variety $\underline{A}^n$ is affine, i.e., a product of a linear mapping and a translation.

13. An affine variety V is said to be <u>rational</u> if k(V) is a purely transcendental extension of k, i.e., there is a transcendence basis $u_1,\ldots,u_n$ for k(V) over k such that $k(V) = k(u_1,\ldots,u_n)$. Show that the classical groups SL_n, SO_n, Sp_n and GL_n are rational varieties. (Hint: which elements of O_n can be written in the form $(1 - A)(1 + A)^{-1}$ with A skew symmetric.) Actually it is possible to show that any connected affine group is a rational variety.

14. Show that if k has characteristic zero, then the affine group G is reductive if and only if it is linearly reductive.

15. Let G be a connected affine group over $\mathbf{C}$. Then G is a complex manifold. Show that $\mathbf{C}[G]$ can be recovered as the set of holomorphic functions f on G such that the right translates of f span a finite dimensional complex vector space. (For the relevant definitions, see Serre, "Lie Groups and Lie Algebras".)